There's a
Snake in
My Cupboard

D0717033

There's a Snake in My Cupboard

*The continuing story
of Kiwoko Hospital
Luwero, Uganda*

Dr Nick Wooding

New Wine Press

New Wine Press
PO Box 17
Chichester
West Sussex PO20 6YB
England

ISBN: 1 903725 54 2

Typeset by CRB Associates, Reepham, Norfolk
Cover design by CCD, www.ccdgroup.co.uk
Printed in England by Clays Ltd, St Ives plc

Contents

	Foreword	7
	Acknowledgments	11
	Introduction	13
Chapter 1	Early Days	17
Chapter 2	Training for Mission	22
Chapter 3	Doctor Livingstone, I Presume?	28
Chapter 4	In at the Deep End	33
Chapter 5	Rules of the Road	39
Chapter 6	Blood Is Thicker than Water	46
Chapter 7	Money and Other Matters	50
Chapter 8	HIV-AIDS	57
Chapter 9	Mothers and Children	69
Chapter 10	A Woman's Work Is Never Done	76

Chapter 11	The Four 'M's: Malaria, Measles, Malnutrition, Meningitis	80
Chapter 12	We Treat, Jesus Heals	87
Chapter 13	Magic and Mismanagement	92
Chapter 14	Landmarks	99
Chapter 15	Education	104
Chapter 16	Power to Live By	110
Chapter 17	VIPs	115
Chapter 18	Close Encounters	123
Chapter 19	Made for Mission	127
Chapter 20	Stress and Satisfaction	134
	Epilogue: Making a Difference	145
Chapter $20\frac{1}{2}$	What Katy Did	150

Foreword

> *Our first responsibility is not to build the Church or even to get souls saved – it is to represent Christ and to bring His message to the world. As God beholds us in Christ, so the world must behold Christ in us. As Christ represents us before the Father, so we must represent Christ before the world.*
>
> (Cornelius Stam, 1909–2003)

This book is a follow-up to Ian Clarke's recently reissued book, *The Man With the Key Has Gone*. It describes the day-to-day experiences of Nick and Kate Wooding in Kiwoko (1997–2003). It does not attempt to cover the period between Ian leaving and Nick arriving; that would require another book!

Like Ian, Nick praises the work of the Ugandan staff and the sacrifices they have made; they are the backbone of the hospital. Nick describes Ian and Robbie Clarke as amazing people; we would describe Nick and Kate in the same way! What they have achieved testifies that Kiwoko continues to be God's work, because his

7

people continue to be faithful. Nick's personal faith and simplicity of living shine out through these pages. His ability to tackle problems, whether to do with administration, illness, social deprivation, or spiritual need, reflect the Great Physician.

To mention only Ian, and Nick and their families would not suffice; we also need to honour the contributions of Richard Montgomery and Donald Brownlie, and their families: Donald followed on from Richard, who followed on from Ian (Donald sadly passed away during the writing of this book, having given a lifetime of service to Africa. This book is in part a dedication to him, a good friend of Kiwoko). The baton now rests with Jim and Margaret McAnlis, and James Nnyonyintono, administrators and medical superintendent respectively. It is a mark of maturity that a Ugandan doctor now heads the medical team.

The 'genealogy of Kiwoko' is a testament of God's faithfulness and unfailing love. It contains the names of Ugandans and expatriates without whom the work would not have prospered; they are an equal part of the work as are those who support and pray for the work from a distance. If you become involved with Kiwoko prepare for change and challenge: God is about! Kiwoko changes lives; it brings people into eternal life; it is a light for God in the surrounding district of Luwero, which has encircled the world. Has it all been plain sailing? Of course not. The faith of those involved has been tested, but God has not failed. Christianity in Uganda, including Kiwoko, is lived out in the raw; people have nothing else to fall back on, to depend on, except God.

The spirit of Kiwoko and the Spirit in Kiwoko is an example to us all. God has given us a key, he has given us Kiwoko; he has given us an engraving tool that writes the word 'Life'.

It remains an honour for us to be associated with Kiwoko Hospital, even in the smallest of ways.

> 'See, I have engraved you on the palms of my hands; your walls are ever before me.'
>
> (Isaiah 49:16)

Ian Taylor
On behalf of Friends of Kiwoko Hospital

Acknowledgments

Note: Some names have been changed for the protection of patients, staff and families.

Introduction

> *The questions which one asks oneself begin, at least, to illuminate the world, and become one's key to the experience of others.*
> (James Arthur Baldwin, 1924–87)

For an African, misfortune does not just happen; there has to be a cause behind it. It would be not enough to say, 'Mosquitoes spread malaria when they bite': a Ugandan would say, 'Yes, but who sent the mosquito to bite me and not that other person, so that I caught malaria and not him?' Offended ancestors may be the cause of misfortune, or a witch-doctor (traditional healer) may have imposed a curse. In the latter case he may have done it from malice or at the behest of someone else who believes him to be the cause of his misfortune. Similarly witchcraft or some outside force may be believed to be the cause of HIV-AIDS, in which case it is unstoppable, so why change one's ways? As part of their project while on elective in Kiwoko some of our medical students asked patients if they had gone to a traditional healer before coming to the hospital; they usually gave the answer the student expected: 'Never', but as the nurses subsequently pointed out, nearly all patients have been to their local healer first.

Is the fault entirely theirs? Surely it also an indictment of missionaries who brought a non-miraculous programmed Western gospel explaining how to get to heaven. The result was a veneer: hearers became 'good church goers', but when misfortune struck they went back to the witch-doctor. The rise of Pentecostalism in Uganda is partly explained by the fact that it has an answer to the problem of suffering: Jesus has overcome the powers of evil and healing can be found in Him.

As I sat reading during our block placement in Uganda from All Nations Christian College, in 1995, I reflected on the health beliefs of the Baganda people; it was not until Kate and I came to Kiwoko that we actually started to understand and see these beliefs in practice, and experience how ingrained they are. When you have nothing at all, any Westerner looks a possible source of livelihood. How can this not influence behaviour and produce 'rice Christians'?

We assume that people will adopt our culture and beliefs if we help them and supply their needs, and we expect that they will conform to our world-view and satisfy our standards. In other words, we expect them to come to and live before God on our terms. In the process it is easy to forget that all of us are prodigals, equally needing grace and mercy and to have our lives reshaped by God. I had to re-examine my own beliefs: those that were based on culture or bigotry, and those that were scriptural. As always happens, Uganda and Ugandans have taught me more than I have given them.

During our time away from home, people with whom I had graduated had prospered and succeeded in their careers while I was learning that it is in laying down your life that you receive life, and, *'whatever you did for one of the least of these brothers of mine, you did for me'*. Like those who preceded us, Ian, Richard and Donald and their families, Kate and I have had to learn 'upside down living'; small is big, least is greatest, weakness is strength. We began to learn, from experience, what life is for and found a new direction and purpose.

Chapter 1

Early Days

> You can give without loving, but you cannot love
> without giving.
> (Amy Carmichael, 1867–1951)

Before applying to medical school I remember discussing the question, 'Why do you want to do medicine?' I think the agreed answer was, 'To help people,' to which the reply might well have been: 'Well, why not be a fireman!' My real reason was different, the same as many of my colleagues, and not nearly as altruistic as the impression I gave: I wanted to have a stable, well-paid job, so that I could be rich, respected and esteemed. In December 1983 I was offered my key to success: a place to read medicine at Oxford University. 'Wonderful,' I thought. Thankfully God had a different agenda. I had been asking the very dangerous question, 'What is meaning of life?' and found the answer at a Billy Graham meeting in 1984 on the pitch at Villa Park, where I met Jesus; it was when I was about to leave school for university.

As I studied and matured my value system began to change; I now wanted to help people and do something of value with my life. In this search for meaning I moved out of my self-centred world: my focus became God-centred, with a growing desire to know Him and help other people to know Him too. It seemed to me that working as a missionary doctor in the developing world would be a suitable outlet for this new sense of calling. Where would I be of most help – surely in a setting where doctors are in scarce supply? My thoughts turned to Africa; I discovered that in Uganda there is only one doctor for every 30,000 people; most doctors practise in cities, so that the ratio was even worse in rural areas. Most people in Uganda have to walk more than five miles to seek help at a health unit; this is usually only a dispensary run by a solitary nurse, with access neither to doctors nor effective medicines.

I was able to put my thoughts to the test in 1989, when I did my medical student elective. Most medical students have the opportunity to spend several weeks abroad, gaining medical experience in a different culture; I wanted to visit Africa and here was my chance. I chose Kuluva, a rural hospital run by the Church of Uganda in the northern part of the country. I decided that if I had a useful and fulfilling time I would become a missionary doctor; otherwise I would stay at home, have 2.2 children and work contentedly as a general practitioner in an inner-city practice. With these thoughts in mind I travelled to Uganda.

I visited even more rural areas of northern Uganda than Kuluva. Dick Ayres, a doctor there, had been invited to teach at a training course for health workers; the meeting was being organised by the Save the Children Fund and was located close to the Sudanese border. Dick invited me along, and since it was such a long way we stayed overnight; I listened as Dick talked and shared stories with other expatriates about life in Africa; it was most entertaining! People who have been overseas generally try to outdo each other in recounting anecdotes and adventures, losing nothing in the retelling. I suppose this is one of the reasons why people who have never travelled or worked abroad find it difficult to relate to missionaries – they just can't compete. As I listened that night two things stood out: firstly, the film *The Gods Must Be Crazy* had become a 'must see', because it portrayed life in Africa; secondly, I started to understand that the most important person in Uganda was neither the President nor the Archbishop, but the person with the key to the drawer containing the stamp for the next necessary document. As Ian Clarke discovered, this person is never around so another official will simply shrug his shoulders and say, 'the man with the key has gone.' To the uninitiated it is ridiculous that there is no one there to deputise; a seasoned missionary would probably shrug his shoulders and say, 'TIA' (this is Africa). This mysterious man with the key can hold up the proverbial multitude; a bribe would bring him scurrying from his hiding place, but this is not a satisfactory option for Christians.

David Hodgson, who was Finance Manager of the hospital, once went into an office to get a vehicle registration document that Sula, our driver, had been unable to obtain. 'I'm too tired too deal with this today, come back tomorrow,' said the official. Easier said than done: it would mean a journey of up to one and a half hours each way. David would not move and asked to see the manager who quickly solved the problem; the official had been looking for a bribe. On another occasion I went into the immigration office to pick up my work permit, but it wasn't ready. 'Come back tomorrow,' was the jovial response. I asked if anyone knew my friend Ian Clarke, who wrote for the Sunday paper; at this point a drawer opened and the work permit mysteriously appeared.

Some of this is understandable: civil servants are often not paid, sometimes because their wages have been siphoned off at a higher level; corruption trickles down through the system. A Ugandan journalist has written a book called *How to Be a Ugandan*. In it he describes how some civil servants leave their jackets over the backs of their chairs to give the impression that they are still around; they then do something else for the rest of the day, something for which they are actually paid. If someone comes looking for them colleagues will say, 'There's his jacket, he can't be far away!' When challenged about the ethics of this practice the answer would be, 'They pretend to pay us, and we pretend to work.' Thankfully things are improving since the initial legacy of those post civil war days.

When I returned to England after my elective one of the first things I did was to hire the video *The Gods Must Be Crazy*, to remind myself of Africa. I had had a fulfilling time, so I decided to become a missionary doctor. This would involve further training and it seemed that general practice (GP) would offer the best all-round experience in preparation for work in a rural African hospital. I suppose I thought that it would be rather like working in a cottage hospital. I applied to a GP scheme in Lewisham, SE London, where I would experience more 'bread-and-butter' medicine than at a teaching hospital. Around that time Kate and I were married. Kate had also spent some time in Uganda in 1989–90, on a youth mission in the Busoga Diocese in south-east Uganda. As I tackled married life and GP practice I forgot about 'the man with the key', but a reminder was on its way.

Chapter 2

Training for Mission

> 'Continuous effort – not strength or intelligence –
> is the key to unlocking our potential.'
> (Black Elk, 1863–1950)

Impatience is a characteristic of youth; with the aware-
ness of so much need it is tempting to cut training short
and get into the meat of things, but this is usually a
mistake. Appropriate training increases usefulness; I
was later to regret shortcomings in aspects of my
training. Expectations are rising in the developing
world: people are no longer satisfied with time-expired
drugs or doctors who learn through practising on fellow
human beings. In addition, most people who go overseas as missionaries will one day return home and need
suitable qualifications to get a job; it is not enough to
say, 'Well, they allowed me to operate in Africa,' to the
College of Surgeons.

Medical skills in themselves are not enough to prepare
for Africa, so after GP training we spent two years at All
Nations Christian College in England, training in biblical

studies and cross-cultural issues. This allowed (forced!) us to evaluate the idea that 'West is best (and forget about the rest)'. At the end of the first year we had the opportunity to carry out a block placement of 8–10 weeks in a mission setting anywhere in the world. I was keen on the so-called 10–40 Window and the Silk Road, a vague idea of a journey ending in Pakistan; however Kate reminded me that before our marriage I had agreed we would return to Uganda. I didn't remember this conversation, but needless to say, Uganda it was! We decided to try a programme called Community Health Evangelism (CHE), which would combine medicine with evangelism; it was now 1995.

The week before we left for Uganda we were baby-sitting for some friends at All Nations Christian College and spotted *The Man With the Key Has Gone* on their bookshelf; according to one of the back-packers' guides it is recommended reading for visitors to Uganda. It tells the story of Ian Clarke, an Irish GP and Christian, who left everything to go to the Luwero Triangle in Uganda. This area had been called the 'Killing Fields of Africa' and in Ian's early days there was plenty of residual evidence of this. During the civil war of 1981–86 in Uganda at least a quarter of a million people were murdered in the Luwero District, an area only half the size of Northern Ireland. Ian went there in 1987 with his wife Robbie and three young children; from humble beginnings beneath a tree they went on to establish a hospital at Kiwoko, subsequently described as one of the best hospitals in Uganda and also the fastest growing. The project moved from the tree, followed by the vestry of the local church and then the first small purpose-built building; it is now a two hundred and twenty bedded hospital with nearly three hundred and fifty staff and students. In addition, it houses an Enrolled Nurse Training School, and a Laboratory Assistant Training School that has regularly trained the top students in the whole country.

Memories of northern Uganda came flooding back as Kate and I picked up Ian's book: the key was starting to turn. We were excited to read about this quality of Christian medical work in the country we were about to visit; perhaps we should take the opportunity to visit Kiwoko? Our first port of call was the CHE programme. Although their programmes are usually excellent this one turned out to be bit of a disaster for us. We travelled to a town called Mukono, where we were lodged in the guesthouse of Livingstone Nkoyoyo, the Archbishop Elect of Uganda. It was a great place, except for some machine gun fire on the first night and the brown swamp water that came out of the tap. Well, at least we had running water. We had attended a course at All Nations about good health abroad and had paid particular attention when the water engineer mentioned that water must be boiled for at least fifteen minutes to sterilise it and destroy all the worm eggs. For eight weeks we drank thoroughly boiled brown water and remained healthy. We felt guilty about using so much electricity to boil the water, so we gave the future Archbishop a donation when we were leaving.

It made us reflect on the importance of clean water. We take it for granted, but much of the world cannot do so. Here are some startling facts:

- 1.1 billion people lack access to clean water.
- Diarrhoeal diseases are a major cause of infant mortality.
- 50,000 people die every day as a result of water-borne and water-related diseases.
- It would cost $9 billion to provide everyone in the world with basic water and sanitation.

Meanwhile:

- $8 billion is spent in the USA on cosmetics every year
- $23 billion per year is spent in Europe on ice-cream.

Our trip to Africa majored more on survival than growth. I worked in a limited way at the local health centre, having broken my right wrist in a football game. A plaster splint makes it very difficult to put on protective gloves for risky procedures such as delivering babies. Perhaps the splint protected me or, more likely, my potential patients.

We tried to find opportunities to travel into the community but were hampered by the co-ordinator. He told us he would collect us for our first day's work at 6.00am, but arrived at 10.00am; we found African time difficult to live with.

Some years later I naively shared my concept of African time with the Bishop of Luwero while we were waiting together for someone to arrive for a meeting. I said, 'I have heard it said somewhere that Westerners have all of the watches but none of the time, and Africans have all of the time but none of the watches.' He probably smiled wryly to himself and then forgave me. I have since learned that my concept of a unique Ugandan time was not entirely correct: most of us fail to be on time some of the time, and some of us, all of the time! Nonetheless, when I was at Kiwoko, I would always complete my ward rounds before rushing to the official District Meeting – it definitely never started on time.

Our worst experience was a trip to the islands on Lake Victoria. We left very early in the morning and before we even arrived at the lake we ran into problems. The co-ordinator hired a *matatu* (taxi) for us, but neglected to agree a price. It is a basic rule in Uganda; always negotiate in advance of entering the vehicle as *muzungu* (whites) are usually overcharged. On arrival at the shores of Lake Victoria, the local police were called to mediate between the taxi driver and our co-ordinator and he ended up having to give away four jerry cans full of fuel that we had bought for the trip.

True to form, the co-ordinator took us round an additional island. The temperature dropped and the lake became choppier by the minute and as we headed for home our consumptive outboard spluttered its last gasps in the darkness. We sat there, bobbing up and down as the pastor tinkered with the engine. The lights of the nearest fishing village now seemed much farther away than before, and life more tenuous. We wondered whether there were crocodiles in the lake, and how big their teeth and jaws were. Perhaps we had chosen the wrong programme.

While we laugh at it all now, this experience affected us so much that I always advised our elective students, 'Be careful travelling by taxi. The islands on Lake Victoria can be dangerous places – even if the guide-book does say it is an amazing experience.' People worry about AIDS when they visit Uganda or other parts of Africa, but they are much more likely to come to grief in a road traffic accident or in the hands of an uncoordinated co-ordinator.

Chapter 3

Doctor Livingstone, I Presume?

> *Small opportunities are often the beginning of great enterprises.*
>
> (Demosthenes, 384–322 BC)

While on our taste-and-see trip to Uganda from All Nations Christian College, Kate joined some friends from the town of Jinja. Simon and Amanda were part of the Busoga Trust, a charity involved in digging wells to provide clean water for the villages. Amanda was having her hair cut at the Sheraton Hotel in Kampala when Kate saw a *muzungu* (white person) carrying a number of copies of *The Man With the Key Has Gone*. He turned out to be on a team led by Ian Clarke at Kiwoko Hospital. The last information we had had about Ian was at the end of his book, at which juncture he was ill with cancer, and we were not aware of the outcome. Kate wrote him a note to say that we wanted to visit, and that this could conveniently be arranged through the Busoga Trust, some of whom were about to visit Kiwoko to discuss the local water situation.

So we got a lift with Andrew Pearson. That is how we first set our eyes on Kiwoko. Our plan had been to do community work, and here we were at a hospital! I suppose that God brought us to Uganda to lead us to Kiwoko, and we had to go through various trials so we would know that it was really his place for us. I would work as a GP after all, involved in a hospital, but one that was involved in community work. As a consequence of the difficulties we had been through I now had a better picture of health care in Uganda. I had worked in a health centre in Mukono and had observed some of the weaknesses of that situation. I had seen two community programmes that looked excellent on paper, but in reality were not effective. I had also been a patient myself, with my broken wrist, and I had met Peter Bewes, an experienced and highly respected Christian doctor, adviser to the Ministry of Health and linked with the Church Missionary Society (CMS). Peter said one thing that struck me, 'Doctors always end up building hospitals, because they know what needs to be done, and if it is not being done they will do it themselves.' How true.

At Kiwoko, Ian Clarke knew that he needed to build a hospital so that, among other things, local mothers would be able to deliver their babies safely without the dangerous and uncomfortable journey to a distant hospital. Some of them would rather die than travel to an expensive place where they did not know anyone. He had to build a hospital in order to meet the unmet medical and surgical needs. He knew he had to build a Christian Hospital to meet the physical and spiritual needs, and he had the faith in God to do so. He had the vision, he saw the need, and he had faith.

When we reached Kiwoko with the Busoga Trust, Ian was there to meet us and took us on a tour of the busy wards. The nurses were caring, diligent and active in their work – such a contrast to what we had previously seen. Whatever was ordered happened! Ian mentioned that they were short-staffed and invited us to join him for a while. He asked Kate what kind of work she could do, if one day we did return to Kiwoko. It really impressed Kate; instead of just wanting a doctor, for which everybody was craving, he was also concerned that she should be fulfilled. We had two weeks left over for a holiday after Mukono, and quickly decided to come to Kiwoko for this remaining time. Ben Khingi was the acting medical superintendent at the time, so Kate offered to help him. He explained that he was struggling to find information in various files. Each medical superintendent up to now had filed things in his own way and the files required unification. It proved to be a very worthwhile time, as two weeks spent trying to sort out the files gave her an insight into the running of the hospital and its history. Some things were intriguing and others amusing. There was a file containing only one letter, not because of its unique importance but because there was no other obvious repository. This file was named 'Chicken' – a letter to the local leader asking him to tell community members to stop letting their chickens roam free in the hospital compound as they were eating all the plants. One of the early Kiwoko expatriates used to catch these chickens and roast them to reinforce the lesson. At first sight this seemed to be a great idea, but I was reliably informed that it was totally unacceptable as local people are poor; a chicken represents a lot of money.

When I became medical superintendent we had the same wandering fowl phenomenon and used to arrest them for suspicious behaviour, take them before the beak, and fine the owners once they came to claim them; this policy was subsequently to rebound on me. In December 1998 we were given a turkey by way of thanks to Kate for finding a person a job. Rob, a building supervisor with Tear Fund, named the turkey Jackie, unaware that I had just employed another Jackie as a medical records clerk. I hoped she wouldn't take it personally if she ever found out. Having Jackie (the turkey) seemed ideal, since we could fatten her up for Christmas. However, the All Nations College syllabus they had not included 'How to look after your turkey'. This turkey had spent its formative years in Eastern Uganda, where they ate millet, and abhorred the diet of Central Uganda, based more on maize flour and stewed bananas. Jackie lived in our house. I would carry her out and tie her to a tree, and then clean up before starting my ward round. At some point later in the day I would see Alice, our house-girl, chasing round the hospital trying to catch the now-escaped bird before I too received a letter. Eventually we gave up and Jackie was killed and put in the freezer. If we had understood turkey culture at the beginning we might have had a more fitting Christmas lunch, instead we were faced with the problem of how to carve four pounds of turkey scraps. The next year we bought a turkey from a nearby village, and had it killed and frozen immediately, having learnt our lesson.

It is said that on meeting someone you form an opinion within the first few minutes. Ian and Robbie Clarke are truly amazing people, and Ian's charisma and energy attracted us immediately. He advised us that if we wanted to come to Kiwoko, a project supported at that time by CMSI (the Church Missionary Society, Ireland), we needed to find an Irish relative somewhere. This was easier said than done: one of Kate's grandmothers was half French, and I had one who was one-eighth Welsh. We failed to find a single drop of Irish blood, so there was nothing for it but to apply to CMS London.

When a doctor senses a call to mission work the world is his oyster, but we believed that God was calling us to Kiwoko. A whole series of events pointed in that direction: the baby-sitting and Ian Clarke's book, the subsequent meeting with someone in Uganda carrying the book; the opportunity to visit Kiwoko; and the resonance within our hearts. Everything seemed to suggest that God wanted us in Kiwoko, not somewhere else; when CMS asked us, 'Will you go anywhere?' we had the confidence to reply 'No, it's Kiwoko or nothing, and if you can't send us there we will have to find someone who can!' That isn't the recommended approach to an interview. CMS graciously agreed to have us, and sent us to Kiwoko.

Chapter 4

In at the Deep End

> When we honestly ask ourselves which person in our
> lives means the most to us, we often find that it is those
> who, instead of giving advice, solutions, or cures, have
> chosen rather to share our pain and touch our wounds
> with a warm and tender hand. The friend who can be
> silent with us in a moment of despair or confusion, who
> can stay with us in an hour of grief and bereavement,
> who can tolerate not knowing, not curing, not healing
> and face with us the reality of our powerlessness, that
> is a friend who cares.
>
> (Henri Nouwen, 1932–96)

It was 1997. Having pushed many doors, Kate and I were
on our way to Kiwoko. I had come to do community-
based health care; in 1998 I would become the medical
superintendent of the hospital, so there would be a steep
learning curve. I had only been in that post for a month
when I had a meeting with the Africa director of an
international donor organisation. He wanted to know
why they had not received a report from us about an

AIDS project they had funded for the past eighteen months, when one was due every six months. Everyone around the table remained silent, and then the chairman, turning towards me, said, 'This is Dr Wooding, he's in charge of that side of things.' I tried to put together an acceptable reason, but failed to convince him that we had done what we had promised – we hadn't. This taught me the lesson: don't mess around with donors. If you have been allocated money for a specific project then make sure that it is used only for that project. In this case the money had not been misused: it had genuinely been spent on AIDS work, but we had no records to prove it. As Christians we must behave and be seen to behave with total integrity. We need to agree any changes to proposals with the other interested parties and not break our promises, which is wrong and results in a loss of trust; and loss of trust, among other things, means loss of funding. The success of Kiwoko has rested in large measure on trust, accountability, and openness. This has meant that existing donors have been more willing to sponsor further projects and to recommend additional support from other organisations.

In terms of management, I had been thrown in at the deep end. There was also the medical deep end. Doctors educated in Britain, unlike their Ugandan counterparts, do not carry out surgical operations without further specialised training. When we arrived at Kiwoko on 14 June 1997, the scalpel and I were relative strangers. I discovered that I was to be on-call twice during the incoming week. I appealed to Donald Brownlie: 'Donald, I'm only a GP, I can't do a caesarean section!' Donald, from Northern Ireland, had spent almost his entire medical career as a missionary doctor in Africa and had succeeded Richard Montgomery as medical superintendent. Moses, a Ugandan doctor with excellent surgical skills, rescued me from my current predicament, covering for my deficiencies while teaching me what to do. I learned the art of caesarean section by assisting him with five and then doing five with him assisting; then I was on my own. At the end of the first month I did my first solo weekend on call, and prayed that I would not have to repair a strangulated hernia. All was well until 10.00pm on Sunday night when the strangulated hernia arrived. Donald encouraged me, 'Have a go and call me if you get stuck.' After five minutes I was well and truly stuck; human anatomy seems much more obvious in diagrams than on the operating table.

My next weekend on call I prayed more urgently that there would be no difficult surgery. At 10.00pm on Sunday a man came in with signs of peritonitis. Once again I discussed the case with Donald and again he advised, 'Have a go.' Donald, I might add, had been in even more isolated situations in Malawi, having to operate by the light of a hurricane lamp with a textbook propped up before him: 'Turn the next page please!' This time Lawrence was working in the operating theatre. Lawrence, who features in *The Man With the Key Has Gone*, is a theatre assistant who had appeared out of the bush when Kiwoko was in process of construction, and had offered his help. Although he is too humble to admit it, he actually instructed many doctors on surgical techniques. Even though he did not do the surgery himself, he would advise the operator, 'You don't want to be doing that, you should try this.' My confidence suitably bolstered by his presence, I was happy to 'have a go'. I followed the recipe from a surgery textbook called *Primary Surgery*, by Peter Bewes; Peter had mentioned this book in 1995 when I consulted him with my fractured wrist. He wrote the book with Maurice King, who is not a surgeon. His essential contribution was to read what Peter had written and comment, 'This is too complicated; if I can't understand it then people in rural areas definitely won't.' So they produced a surgical textbook written in simple language that anyone could understand.

As we put our patient to sleep I suddenly remembered that any patient with acute pain in the abdomen should be questioned about their alcohol intake, since one of the possible diagnoses is acute pancreatitis, for which surgery is contra-indicated. I quickly asked him if he drank alcohol; as he dropped off to sleep he seemed to mumble, 'Yes'. As I opened him up pus came pouring out!

'I really don't know what I'm doing.' I panicked to myself. I proceeded to delve into the abdominal cavity, pulling out huge loops of bowel looking for the expected perforation, but without success. Lawrence, who had seen it all before, offered some advice. 'I'm the doctor, I must make the decisions.' I reminded myself as I continued pulling the same loops of bowel out with greater vigour; and pushing them back in again. Eventually I gave in. Lawrence felt around the stomach and said, 'Doctor, here is the problem.'

'A perforated stomach ulcer?' I mused.

'No, doctor,' replied Lawrence, 'it's the pancreas.'

At least I had been right to think of pancreatitis, but then the pressing problem was, what should I do next? When I consulted Lawrence he seemed disconcertingly uncertain. Then we did what all great missionary bush doctors do; we opened the textbook and read the section on how to drain a pancreatic abscess. I put on another pair of gloves and did what it said, 'Irrigate the pancreas and insert a drain'. The bit about placing a feeding tube in the jejunum (upper small intestine) was beyond my rudimentary skills, so I simply closed the incision.

According to the textbook, a ruptured pancreatic abscess has a mortality rate of 30%–50%, so it seemed likely that the patient would die. Against all expectations he survived, so my single-case series survival rate is 100%! We do not work alone; we trust in God and pray before every operation: God was the unseen surgeon who got me out of trouble. None of the UK doctors had formal surgical training; we learned on the job because there was no alternative. Even the really sick usually made it off the operating table alive. During my six years I can remember only three deaths during surgery, each related to the anaesthetic. We responded to this need by sending a nurse for formal training as an anaesthetic officer. Consultant anaesthetists are in short supply in Uganda.

One of the frustrating parts of the work in the early days was the contrast between what needed to be done and what I was able to do. That is why training is so important. Another frustration was doing medicine through a translator, since I never became fluent enough in the local language, Luganda, to take a full history (except maybe for malaria in children) and therefore had to ask questions through someone else. My broken Luganda helped when the nurse asked a different question from the one I had asked, or the patient gave an answer that was not correctly translated. However, sometimes the patient did not speak Luganda but only another of the tribal languages of which there are forty-six in Uganda. The nurse would then have to find a second translator who might be another patient or visitor. Failing that we sometimes had to resort to asking one of the security guards who could speak Swahili. Many of the northerners speak Swahili, but fewer local people do. Those who do know Swahili are usually a bit reluctant to let this be known because it now has negative associations; it was the army language and the soldiers had violated the people for five years during the war.

Many patients, especially women, suffer from psycho-somatic problems and depression; good history taking is vital in these circumstances, involving detailed exploration and explanation, so that an adequate consultation could take a long time. Education, including preventative medicine, is best left in the hands of native speakers.

Chapter 5

Rules of the Road

> *'... if you're driving down the highway in the middle of the night and you see a sign that says "Bridge Out", pray for some intellectual understanding of that message, or you're going to have an experience you'll never forget!'*
>
> (Dag Hjalmar Agné Carl Hammarskjold, 1905–61)

Taxis in Uganda are not like London black taxis, but an array of senescent machines varying from cars to vans to pick-ups. Drivers may have obtained their driving licence; then again, they may not. Even if they are proficient drivers, there are still the roads and the other drivers to deal with. Vehicles, including taxies, are usually poorly maintained, if at all, so stopping distances are unpredictable. For cultural reasons, no one blows the whistle on a colleague on almost any issue, including the roadworthiness of a vehicle or driver; it is only after someone has been dismissed or has left or has been injured or killed, that the truth emerges.

Edward was one driver I encountered at Kiwoko Hospital. He had injured an eye, but his subsequent eye test had been faked so that he could continue in his job. He was driving me to a clinic when he had his first accident. He was speeding along the road in the mud during the rainy season and lost control. Thankfully we were in the Land Rover ambulance. I was in the front with the microscope on my lap. We mounted a bank and the microscope escaped through the open window. We continued up the bank and were soon airborne – like a stunt from a Hollywood film. Hitting a termite mound in the bush we were deflected towards the road, where we made a surprisingly soft landing. Unfastening my protective seatbelt, I got out and, trembling, climbed the hundred yards along the road to retrieve the microscope that, amazingly, was still in one piece. We could not proceed on our journey as the bumper was deeply entwined with a wheel. Eventually a passing moped driver took pity on us, produced a spanner and removed the bumper. We carried on to the clinic with the bumper tied to the roof rack. Edward was given a yellow card warning; if he crashed again he would be sacked; he did and he was; life is precious.

Pick-up trucks carry an amazing number of people. This is especially true when villagers travel to a neighbour's funeral in a far away district. The unlicensed driver usually feels that it is important to participate in the spirit of the funeral. Well tanked up with home brew provided at the funeral, he drives the mourners back, consoling them; that is, if they ever get home. This is why, in Uganda, funerals beget funerals.

Taxi drivers travel incredibly fast to reach their destination before the passengers come out of shock; they then restock and race back equally quickly. The philosophy behind this is that the quicker you go the less likely you are to have an accident in any one spot. It is possible, even for the less observant, to discern specific rules of the road in Uganda:

1. *Blind overtaking*. If you are overtaking, make sure that it is on a blind corner or just below the brow of a hill.
2. *The killer coach*. Right of way belongs to the strongest. If it is a cross-country bus (the killer coach), vacate the road.
3. *The sacred cattle priority*. Cows are unversed in the *Highway Code*, knowing only how to use their horns. When roaming the highways and verges they have rights of way and rumination.
4. *Save electricity*. Do not switch your lights on when it is dark – this will waste the battery and give away your position to oncoming vehicles.
5. *Use every special sense*. If it is night time and a single light approaches, listen carefully for the sound of a truck with only one headlight working.
6. *Blind your opponent*. Put your main beam on when passing a vehicle. This enables the next oncoming coach to make a blind approach.
7. *Never ask directions*. Most people in rural areas cannot drive; if asked for directions they will send you down a narrow pathway (entirely scriptural) when there is a very large road close by.

8. *Elastic mile rule*. If you are giving someone a lift, be careful when they say they are just going down the road – the 'just' can turn into fifty miles.

9. *Take a picnic*. Taxis are only licensed to carry fourteen passengers in the first layer; luggage may include fish, DIY articles, hens and the odd cockerel. You will not go hungry or unsoiled.

10. *It's the vehicle's fault*. If something goes wrong, it is never the driver's or the rider's fault. The inanimate becomes animate: I once had a patient who had a bicycle accident (he was struck by a car), because he was riding at midnight without lights and he was drunk. I asked him what happened and he replied, 'The bike threw me.' I asked him if it was fair to blame the bike when he was a black man wearing dark clothes on a dark night riding a black bike with no lights. He did not see my point. 'No doctor, the bike threw me.'

11. *Don't stop at accidents*. If you hit someone, never stop to help or you might be lynched. Go to the nearest police station and ask for sanctuary.

Bearing all this in mind, if possible, use an experienced driver, but choose him carefully.

During our time in Kiwoko two of our staff died in road traffic accidents. During our time Kampala also got a hearse, seen driving round with a siren on the top. It was once spotted in a traffic jam, so the lights started flashing. One observer commented, 'People rush to their deaths, and then they rush to their funeral!'

Accident! Accident!

The following account by Esther Bawuba, medical officer at Kiwoko hospital, gives a dramatic picture of activity after a major road traffic accident:

One quiet Wednesday night, I had finished going around the wards while on call. Let me settle down, I thought to myself. Suddenly a nurse knocked on my door disturbing me. I called out that I was on my way. I thought it was the usual minor accident, and planned to work very fast and then go back to sleep. I soon found out how mistaken I was!

There was blood everywhere and injured people all over the place. Some of them were groaning, others were quarrelling, and others were shouting and fighting. Most of the hospital staff were awake by that time and busily at work. People were dashing here and there in a mêlée, trying to identify their relatives. Patients were being triaged quickly in the hope of saving lives; so many patients.

'Get the stretcher.'

'Measure the blood pressure.'

'This patient needs surgery, now.'

The ambulance shuttles between the scene of the accident and the hospital, bringing in more and more victims. One patient is dealt with and nurses bring four more! Nearly all the casualties are adults (they have all been involved in one of those multiple vehicle pile-ups that are always waiting to happen on Ugandan roads). The whole hospital is beavering away as if it is daytime. We work most of the night; sleep is forgotten in the effort to save lives. Our teamwork was good; God rewarded our efforts, and many of the people who reached hospital survived.

Godfrey, a twenty-six-year-old businessman, married with three children, was one who survived. It had been around 10.00pm when the two taxis collided on the main road to Kampala. Godfrey was in a third taxi that stopped and he, with others, began to help the victims, many injured, stranded, and confused. As they did so, a lorry from Kampala sped towards them; the driver decided that they were robbers, not Good Samaritans, and drove right through them. In all, a total of forty-three people died in that accident. Godfrey lost his right leg and would never have been able to afford treatment and the prosthesis. Because Kiwoko Hospital has a Good Samaritan fund to help the poor and destitute, we were able to help a Good Samaritan who was in need. Godfrey bought us a Bible with the money he had brought, about £4, in gratitude for the love and care he had received.

Tumusiime, a twenty-three-year-old woman, was an accident victim who did not survive. She was brought into hospital, comatose and with fractures of both legs; there were no relatives with her. Usually, to minimise costs, patients bring an attendant to the hospital with them to cook and wash their clothes. It was only after some days that Tumusiime's mother discovered that her daughter had been involved in an accident; she came rushing to the hospital, not knowing whether her daughter was dead or alive; to her great relief she was still alive and the hospital staff were taking care of her. She kept on thanking the staff for their care, but Tumusiime's head injury was very serious and her condition deteriorated. At first the mother refused to let us transfer Tumusiime, because she considered that the quality of care at Kiwoko was much better than in any other hospital. At last she allowed her to be transferred to the care of a neurosurgeon and as the ambulance sped towards Kampala she prayed all the way, watching her daughter and hoping she would survive. Unfortunately, Tumusiime died a few days later in Mulago Hospital, the government hospital in Kampala that provides regional services.

Chapter 6

Blood Is Thicker than Water

> *My friend I consider you my brother. I know we are not blood, and blood is thicker than water, but your body already has all the blood it needs. You will always need water.*
>
> (Eric Pio, poet)

Major accidents are common and can exhaust the hospital's store of banked blood in a single night. Blood was obtained once a week from the main blood bank in Kampala but was always in scarce supply. There were donors who gave regularly – people known to have lifestyles that did not put them at risk of HIV. If blood was needed urgently, a relative or even a passer-by would be asked to donate. The risk of HIV in un-screened donors is 6%; even with an HIV test the risk is 2%, because there is a period when the virus is active but antibody levels are too low to be recorded.

Malaria is another condition that necessitates blood transfusion. The malaria season occurs twice a year; the parasites invade the red blood cells causing them to burst, resulting in severe anaemia. Children are most severely affected, having less immunity and also a smaller blood volume, and can develop heart failure because of the anaemia. Before coming to hospital they have often had inadequate treatment at a health clinic with chloroquine, to which the malaria parasite is now resistant; by the time we see them they have become critically ill. Time and time again we have had the sadness of seeing a child dying of severe anaemia within ten minutes of arrival, but we have also had the joy of seeing others arrive in time to receive life-saving blood transfusions.

One malaria season coincides with school holidays, thus reducing access to one of the main groups of blood donors, young adults. Under extreme pressures I requested hospital staff to give blood to save a life, as I also sometimes did myself.

When Richard Montgomery was medical superintendent, a surgical emergency arose when there were some visitors in the hospital. One of the visitors was asked to give blood, voluntarily of course! More was needed, so the second visitor responded. Finally the surgeon gave some of his blood before completing the operation.

This is an account by a British medical student, on an elective, of a personal experience with blood donation:

> Knock, knock. I jumped up from my sleep and saw a torch shining through my window. I was rather suspicious, since it was my first week in the village and I did not know who it was, or what was going on. 'Are you O-positive?' the nurse asked, for the

third time. At that time of night I found it impossible to understand the question. Then the nurse explained that there had been a serious accident and there were a large number of casualties who urgently needed blood. Five minutes later, along with other students, I was in the laboratory having my blood group checked. We were all still getting used to the fact that we weren't dreaming. It was amazing to realise that we had been through five years of medical school and still did not know our own blood groups. A-positive, AB ... then one, no two of us, had the precious O-positive group that was needed. One unit of blood lighter, we both went to the wards to see if we could be of any use.

It was like nothing we had ever experienced before. In England, at any emergency, medical students are pushed into the background to observe from a safe distance. Now we were actively involved and, scarily, had to apply some of the theoretical knowledge we had gained in medical school. We distributed ourselves between the male and female wards and the theatre, and one of us helped Dr Mandy take two head injury patients to Mulago Hospital in Kampala. After the initial panic, we worked together, prioritising casualties and stabilising patients for surgery, obtaining as much advice as we could from the doctors. It was the first time we had really had to take responsibility, without senior supervision. Before we knew, it was 5.00am. It was only then, as the adrenaline rush wore off, that we realised just how tired we all were; we still had the energy to go home and talk about our experiences; some of us even managed to get up at 8.15am for morning prayers!

Genesis 9 talks about lifeblood. The oxygen rich red blood corpuscles are necessary to life. Blood is a gift of life but one day, as the doctor on duty, I was called on to decide who should receive that gift, a child with life threatening anaemia or a mother with AIDS who had a dependent family. We had only half a unit of blood left and had been unable to find a suitable blood donor for any more. Half a unit of blood is a significant amount for a child as compared to an adult; I concluded that the blood would be best used for the child and transfused it. The woman died and we took her body to her home in Matembe. I felt I needed the wisdom of Solomon that day and thankfully never had to make a similar decision again. It was the one and only time we were unable to locate a suitable blood donor.

Like blood, oxygen itself has been a lifesaver. We bought oxygen concentrators at £1,000 each but with constant use only half of them were in working condition at any one time. Electrical equipment has a more limited lifespan in Uganda as a consequence of frequent power cuts and voltage fluctuations, even though we use voltage stabilisers. Modern, complex equipment cannot cope with voltage fluctuations; sometimes older is better.

Chapter 7

Money and Other Matters

> *The future is like heaven, everyone exalts it, but no one wants to go there now.*
> (James Arthur Baldwin, 1924–87)

Saving for the future is not part of Ugandan culture. Why save when you might die tomorrow and someone else will benefit? State funded health care systems have failed to match demands even in developed countries, and this is even more the case in Uganda. Other approaches, such as health insurance, are required. We introduced Community Based Health Insurance (CBHI), in partnership with the Centre International de Développement et de Recherche (CIDR), a French organisation with many years of experience in this area, so that people could set aside money from the coffee harvest to provide insurance for a whole year. The annual subscription was only £1.50, within everyone's means. However, many people still refused to join, preferring to risk a larger bill in the uncertain future. Some subscribers who did not fall sick became disillusioned and did not rejoin the scheme; they complained that they had not received value for money, since they had not been sick.

Another inhibiting factor in setting up CBHI in Luwero was the legacy of the war between 1981–86, when there was mass murder and society was completely destroyed. I became very aware of this when I visited a gravesite with the British High Commissioner in 2003; most of the local people had lost at least one loved one.

Family expectations are another impediment to saving. If needy relatives turn up it is your duty to provide for them, whether for hospital bills or school fees. People living in the bush sometimes send their children to stay with their urban-dwelling relatives because they are perceived to be rich. The original family members often refuse to have the children back unless they are paid. However, despite all these problems, we have found that CBHI to have been an important way of changing attitudes and persuading people to save.

Lack of money can also increase the temptation to steal. For example, a manager may borrow money from his employers to meet a pressing need, perhaps under pressure from a relative, assuming that he will be able to repay it from future salary without being found out. Another crisis may then interpose so that the money is never returned. Sometimes the root cause is corruption, rather than need. One of our nursing students, who had money for his fees from an expatriate sponsor, handed in a block of wood at the cash office. When it was pointed out that this was not money, he feigned surprise and protested that the money must have been bewitched and turned into the lump of wood! It amazes me that Uganda, reputedly a Christian country, where the East African Revival made such an impact, is also the second or third most corrupt country in the world (according to Transparency International, a South African research group, in 2002).

The poor often delay seeking medical help. I was once on call when a woman presented with a ruptured uterus. I asked her why she had waited so long before she came. The reply made me realise the predicament of the poor and, especially, poor women. This woman's husband told me that her contractions had disappeared and he knew that she was in trouble; he spent all morning getting her to a dispensary, and they referred her on. He then hired a motorbike to get her to the main road. Following this they took two taxis, changing en-route at Luwero. He could see that his wife was getting weaker and concluded that he would soon be returning home with her dead body, to arrange a funeral. Her womb had ruptured and the baby was dead, lying free in her abdomen, outside the womb, along with the placenta that had sustained his life. She underwent emergency surgery; it was touch and go at one point during the operation as her blood pressure dropped to half the normal, but, thankfully, she survived. It could all have been avoided if she had come earlier. They lived in a very remote place and maybe he thought he could not afford a hospital delivery. He may not have known about the Good Samaritan fund available for the poor and needy, the destitute and those without hope. And anyway, she'd been fine giving birth before, hadn't she? Sadly, many Ugandan women die in pregnancy from treatable conditions.

On one particular day I was at a planning meeting with CIDR, when I was asked to deal with an emergency. There were two other doctors who had just completed their houseman's year, but had not realised earlier that they could delegate upwards to me! By the time they did, the case had become very complicated. The patient was a twenty-year-old woman, already in her fourth pregnancy, who lived only three miles away. She had been in labour, with twins, for the whole day and had delivered the first one seven hours before. As is the case with two-thirds of the women in Uganda, she had relied on a traditional birth attendant, a local person who delivers the babies in the village, often without formal training. The second twin was in the transverse position (head and feet sideways) and so could not be delivered in the normal way. Her womb had ruptured, the baby was dead, and she was in shock. I abandoned the meeting and took her to theatre, where the disastrous situation quickly became evident. Sometimes the rupture is like a small tear, but this was as if a small explosion had occurred inside her and torn everything apart. There was a big hole in the uterus, another in the bladder, the urethra (the tube that takes urine from the bladder to the outside) was torn in two places, and a ureter (the tube connecting the kidney to the bladder) was also torn in two. We tried to repair the damage but found it impossible; not even *Primary*

Surgery could help me in this situation. We stopped the bleeding, and stabilised her circulation by means of a blood transfusion and sent her in our ambulance to Mulago Hospital in Kampala, about an hour and a half away. Peter Sserwadda, one of our doctors who had just returned from a meeting in Kampala, went straight back with the patient to care for her en route and to explain the situation. After a month she was returned to us, leaking urine out of the large hole that they had not been able to repair, but at least she was alive. Later, in fact, Peter went for training in surgery and is now the resident surgeon at Kiwoko.

This episode helped me realise why the mission hospital sector, which provides 40%–50% of all the health care in Uganda, is so important. Her tragedy was that she was poor. She could not afford to pay bribes in the government hospital in order to get prompt treatment. She probably delayed coming to Kiwoko, believing that she would require an operation that she could not afford. So she lost her child and will be unable to have others. She may leak urine for the rest of her life and become a social outcast. What a false economy, but it is so common in this community. Her village did not participate in the CBHI scheme. Had they done so all this would have been prevented; she would have had no anxiety about funding her treatment. In any case we would have treated her free of charge in order to save the life of her baby and preserve her own her health; also she lived nearby and we had an available ambulance.

Talemwa was two months old. His mother, an unmarried teenager, had been raped, and then rejected by her family because she became pregnant. A potential husband from her tribe would expect to marry a virgin, so that her prospects of marriage were poor. She had been left, without resources, to care for the child, and now he had developed pneumonia. He made a good recovery; we wrote off her bill and gave her enough money to travel home, fifty miles away. Sadly it illustrates an all too common problem affecting the poor and, especially, vulnerable young women.

Kasozi was a cattle keeper from the Masindi area, about a hundred miles away from Kiwoko. He made the long journey at the advice of a neighbour who had been a patient at Kiwoko Hospital, after two nearer hospitals had not been able to solve his problem. Kasozi was an alcoholic, now complicated by pancreatitis and diabetes. Following treatment, we found it difficult to persuade him to leave as he found life in the hospital to his liking. He needed to take regular medicine for his diabetes but, even more, he needed a change in lifestyle to prevent further complications. His family refused to answer our letters, take responsibility for him, or pay for his treatment. We paid his bills and shared the gospel with him, knowing that he would need God's strength for that radical change. So, we were able to communicate God's love to him in both word and action, leaving the ultimate responsibility with Kasozi. We are grateful for all the prayers and gifts that enabled us to practise medicine in a holistic way, ministering to body, soul, and spirit, and reaching into the surrounding community.

Just before the elections on 1 March 2001 fees at government hospitals were abolished. Paying fees had been known as cost sharing, as people would pay a small contribution to their health care. Money raised in this way helped to cover the cost of some drugs and to pay an extra allowance to the workers, as an encouragement. When government fees were abolished huge numbers of patients transferred to their hospitals for free treatment; we wondered how Kiwoko hospital would fare in these new circumstances. Quite soon the local government hospitals began to run out of essential drugs and sutures, and they were unable to perform even simple operations. Some had to lay off many of their staff. As government units ran out of money, they could only give advice and refer patients to a clinic to buy their own drugs. Of course this was of no use to those who needed surgery and soon the flow of patients went into reverse. Some nights we were doing two or three caesarian sections for women who had been referred from our local government hospital. Tragedies occurred; cases of foetal distress arrived on transfer from a hospital more than thirty minutes drive away. They had needed immediate caesarean sections, but by the time they arrived it was too late and the babies were dead. To make matters worse, caesarean section was still required, so several mothers were left with scars but no children. Patient numbers increased to such an extent that we had to find extra beds and, even then, some patients had to lie on the ward floors. Effectively, we were doing the work of two hospitals and patient numbers increased by about 50%. Thankfully after a couple of months the Government found some extra money and it settled down.

Chapter 8

HIV-AIDS

> *From the point of view of the pharmaceutical industry,*
> *the AIDS problem has already been solved. After all, we*
> *already have a drug which can be sold at the incredible*
> *price of $8,000 an annual dose, and which has the*
> *added virtue of not diminishing the market by actually*
> *curing anyone.*
>
> (Barbara Ehrenreich, b. 1941)

Worldwide, at the end of 2004, more than 39.4 million people were HIV positive; the vast majority (25.4 million) living in Sub-Saharan Africa. Also in 2004, according to UNAIDS, it was estimated that of the 4.9 million people who contracted HIV, 3.1 million were living in Sub-Saharan Africa. This is over 8,000 every day in Sub-Saharan Africa acquiring HIV. 57% of the sufferers are women and girls.

If people were asked what they know about Uganda they would generally mention Idi Amin or AIDS; this is unfortunate, for Uganda is a beautiful and fertile country with friendly and outgoing people. HIV-AIDS has been and remains a problem; Ugandans in their twenties and thirties, who should be the main breadwinners in society, are dying from AIDS, and grandparents have to care for the children. In contrast to most other African countries, the Ugandan authorities acknowledged the problem at an early stage and have taken steps to tackle it. Of those who attended for HIV tests before marriage at Kiwoko in 2000, as now recommended by both Church and State, 13% of men and 14% of women were HIV positive, but thankfully this is now on the decline. In 1995 overall HIV prevalence was about 30%, but was about 6.1% in 2003. One of the reasons for this is that Government policy is to promote a healthy lifestyle, abstaining from sex until married, rather than recommending safe sex by using a condom. Sex is never safe if you or your partner has AIDS. Mrs Museveni, the First Lady and wife of President Yoweri Museveni, is a strong Christian. She gave the following message, based on ABC:

A   Abstain from sex until married.
B   Be faithful to your partner
C   Use a condom if you cannot do A followed by B.

All social groups are affected, as illustrated by this story. A Church of Uganda clergyman attended with a persistent fever. He denied the possibility of AIDS, but eventually allowed me to carry out the test; it was positive. When I asked him if he had been unfaithful to his wife he replied, 'Of course Doctor, I am an African!'

The consequences of HIV infection extend far beyond the individual, to the extended family and surrounding community. The husband is usually the first to be infected, through extramarital relations. Alcoholism is a commonly associated problem, as alcohol diminishes sexual restraint and so increases the risks of contracting HIV and other sexually transmitted diseases. Alcohol abuse leads to so many social and health problems that the Church of Uganda requires members to practise total abstinence. His wife then contracts the virus and transmits it to her children, and the next generation becomes infected. Elderly grandparents are then faced with responsibility for the whole stricken family. There are therefore major social factors and consequences. The virus can affect the brain causing mental illness as well.

Children make up 16% of the total cases of HIV infection in Uganda, having contracted the infection either during pregnancy, during birth, or when breast-feeding. Relatively cheap drugs can reduce the risk of transmission from mother to baby and, consequently, mothers are often keen to have the test. Their husbands' permission is required, but often refused. The reasoning often goes as follows, 'If she is positive then so am I. Since I do not want to know, so neither should she.' The child's welfare is not even considered.

Even if the mother knows that she is HIV positive it can be very difficult to persuade her not to breast feed, as the alternative is to use expensive formula milk, often contaminated with dirty water. Nammata Grace's story illustrates the problem. We saw her first when she was about a year old, having been ill for the previous month.

In spite of being breast fed by her mother she appeared severely malnourished. Grace's mother had the tell-tale skin nodules of Kaposi's sarcoma, a consequence of AIDS, on her face, and Grace was HIV positive. Sometimes a positive test is due to the antibodies being transmitted in the breast milk, rather than being an actual infection, and we hoped that Grace's HIV status would become negative over time. All efforts to improve her weight failed. TB is a common complication of AIDS so we decided on a trial of treatment; within a week her weight was beginning to improve and she was soon able to leave hospital. However, she remained HIV positive after six months and eventually died, her little body unable to cope with the burden of disease.

People with HIV are more likely to fall sick because their immune systems are compromised, making them vulnerable to other infections and to cancers. It is therefore no surprise that Kiwoko Hospital treats many patients who are HIV positive, with a much higher incidence than in the general population. Apart from surgical and obstetric admissions 50–60% of the adult inpatients are HIV positive. About 12.5% of mothers attending the antenatal clinic are HIV positive, similar to the national figures. There are other casualties of AIDS. In my six years at Kiwoko Hospital from 1997 to 2003, I counted thirteen deaths among our staff and students, and most were AIDS related. We treat everyone with compassion and without adopting a judgmental attitude, and at the same time promote healthy lifestyles.

Nanyombi was fifteen years old and pregnant for a second time. When she was fourteen she had had a premature baby boy, cared for in our special care baby unit (SCBU). After a promising start he died later in the village, largely because the poor girl was too immature to care for him. She is pregnant again but the father is a different person. She is playing Russian roulette with AIDS.

Nandyose Lydia was a little ten-year-old girl who came to Kiwoko in March 2001. She was very ill, with diabetes, a heart condition, stunted growth and slight mental retardation. Both her parents had died from AIDS several years previously, but she was HIV negative; now she lived with her grandmother, who was not looking after her very well. She often came barefoot to the diabetic clinic, started by Linda Hodgson a practice nurse from the UK. Lydia was poorly dressed and very hungry having walked, often alone, the twenty kilometres from her home. We would give her clothes and shoes, and pay her taxi fare home. We taught her older sister how to give the insulin injections twice a day, but her medical problems grew worse and her admissions more and more frequent. At first she refused to smile, but with time she became much happier and was usually cheerful, in spite of the pain of the injections and the other treatments. Eventually she succumbed from heart disease. She had become part of our Kiwoko family; those who cared for her miss her, and her laughter. You cannot care for people without sharing and entering into their suffering.

Rather than waiting for patients with AIDS to fall sick, we began to go to the local villages twice a week to visit people with HIV or full-blown AIDS, following their discharge from hospital; more than 100 people were registered for this service. Simple measures such as improving nutrition and treating infections early can reduce the frequency of hospital admissions and improve the quality of life. They had to agree to live in a responsible way; this involved accepting their condition and remaining celibate. As we visited the community we were also able to follow up and care for the orphans.

In an attempt to benefit AIDS sufferers we purchased a plot of land on which they could grow crops. It served as a form of occupational therapy and physiotherapy and the hospital bought the resulting produce for the staff kitchen. It did not generate a great deal of money but when these AIDS patients were treated, they now felt they had earned it by their work. We wanted to support people in a way that increased dignity. Donors who hand out free treatment without responsibility from the recipients can turn them into beggars, which is dehumanising. The hospital still subsidised the workers, but they had an increased sense of self-worth and they were more inclined to take advantage of other support measures offered by the hospital.

Sometimes circumstances can be managed to produce a win/win situation for everyone concerned. One man had broken an arm and had sought help from a traditional bonesetter. Several months later he came to Kiwoko hospital with his arm fixed to the side of his chest and the muscles of his arm had so wasted away through disuse that he could no longer work. Fred Mutyaba, a consultant orthopaedic surgeon who visited the hospital once a month, concluded that his arm could not be improved. The patient agreed to sell us some of his land releasing some of his capital, and the land we allocated for use by AIDS sufferers for another income generating project.

Visitors often come to see the hospital. We try to give them some opportunity to learn something of the surrounding community. They often find it challenging and distressing to see what life is like in the villages. Many return to the hospital overwhelmed by the poverty and deprivation they have witnessed. However, they also find that these trips were the most moving and meaningful parts of their visits. In the West we expect Social Services to take care of people, but in Uganda it is the family's responsibility. This becomes very difficult when AIDS has already devastated the family unit. People switch off to the pain and suffering they see repeatedly on television. First-hand experience makes all the difference.

Here are some typical case histories taken from our AIDS support programme.

We visit a family and find the mother, Nakalanzi, lying under a tree; she is very weak. There are four children; two boys aged thirteen and ten, and two younger children aged six and four. None of the children attend school; they live together in the kitchen as the rest of the house is falling down, and the rain leaks in everywhere. Nakalanzi has painful mouth ulcers caused by HIV infection and is unable to eat anything. She can drink tea, but because the family has no money she cannot even afford sugar to put in it. The rest of the family survives on the food that the two older boys grow in the garden. Nakalanzi knows that she is very sick and will soon die. She is extremely worried about what will happen to her four children; there is no one else to care for them.

In another home is a three-year-old girl who is HIV positive; she had been treated at Kiwoko for ear and skin infections, secondary to AIDS. Such children are often malnourished and in addition suffer from TB. Treating this and providing nourishment can add years to their short lives.

At another house an uncle brings us his nephews. He is very worried about them since their parents both died of AIDS. Unable to cope, he has left them to fend for themselves in a small hut beside his home. The older boy, aged thirteen, earns a little money by digging for other people, but mostly they survive by stealing food from neighbours' gardens; if they are caught their lives will be even tougher.

At another home, a lady in her twenties lies huddled on the ground next to her hut. She is deaf and dumb and also HIV positive. Her three sisters, who were also deaf and dumb, have died; the same man slept with all four women, infecting them. The woman now lives with her only surviving sibling, who is also deaf and dumb, and there are many problems in communicating with them. A neighbour who has been caring for the sick woman has been called away on an urgent matter. Through signing the woman indicates that she has not been able to eat or wash for days, as she is too weak to prepare food or fetch water. Then she starts to cry; what do you do next?

The team visits another family nearby. Kasule, the father, is HIV positive and looks sick. His wife is also HIV positive and is in Kiwoko Hospital, so he is looking after the three children by himself. Only one, a three-year-old girl, is his own, and she looks sick and is probably HIV positive as well. All of them sit on the mud floor; the little girl sucks listlessly at her fingers, and then has diarrhoea all over the floor. The man cleans it up with some leaves and sprinkles sand on the floor. The other two children, aged six and eight (from the wife's previous marriage), sit silently watching. The holes in their T-shirts are as big as their stomachs. They cannot attend school because they have to look after the sick child to allow the father to care for his wife at the hospital. He has a garden where he used to grow food, but it is far from his home and now he is too weak for the task. He has had to sell eight of his ten cows to get money for necessities. Everything is causing him anxiety and he is especially worried about his sick child, who is the only one from his current marriage. To make matters worse, he believes that God is punishing him because this is his third marriage. We treat the child and arrange for an HIV test. When we return later, the man is very happy to see us. 'If you hadn't come to see me and hadn't treated my child,' he says, 'the child would have died.' He is even happier when we are able to tell him that the child is HIV negative. She is ill because her sick and impoverished parents could not adequately feed and care for her.

Nabunnya, who is HIV positive, had been in hospital with tuberculosis at an earlier stage in her pregnancy.

She had been discharged but, having no money for her medical bills, stayed around the hospital hoping that her husband would come with money. While waiting she developed labour pains; the babies were found to be lying transversely in the abdomen, making normal birth impossible. She was given an anti-retroviral drug to prevent transmission of HIV during birth, and the two beautiful babies, a boy, Wasswa, weighing 1.98kg and a girl, Nakato, weighing 1.86kg were delivered by caesarean section. Breast-feeding was avoided, to reduce the likelihood of transmission of the virus, and the babies initially thrived. However, more problems followed as a result of a breakdown in relationship between Nabunnya and her husband. She had no money to buy powdered milk and abandoned the twins, leaving her husband to care for two young babies. He had neither money nor work and was in dire straits, so we helped him. The babies were fed, and the Good Samaritan Fund paid the medical bills. Sadly Wasswa died and the father took him home for burial. Nakato, who has good prospects for long-term survival, accompanied him so that there is some light in an otherwise gloomy story.

Sarah, seventeen years old, presented to the hospital with fever. She had recently had a baby at home. A week later we confirmed that she had full-blown AIDS, implying that she had been infected with HIV several years previously. This sometimes happens when a man with AIDS 'befriends' a young girl in the belief that his condition will be cured by having sexual intercourse with a healthy person. There is, of course, no basis to this belief, but a desperate person may clutch at a straw, ignoring the risk of destroying someone else. Teachers sometimes behave in this way and, even though it is illegal, often escape the consequences by making a payment to the girl's family. Some people are even told by traditional healers that the cure for AIDS is to have sex with a three-year-old.

A recent survey in Uganda reported that 22% of primary school children were sexually active and that 50% of secondary school children had had more than one sexual partner. Young girls are subject to peer pressure. They may be told that without sex their breasts will not develop, or a friend may say, 'Life without sex is like tea without sugar.' We have responded to this challenge by setting up Adolescent Reproductive Health Centres/Youth Clubs. Moral foundations are established and the young people are given appropriate practical information, and find a sympathetic listening ear in the context of a safe environment. We have begun to receive invitations from schools and communities, to teach this vulnerable group of young people the same message, based on Christian values and lifestyle.

Seven Scripture Union groups had been started in local schools before we left for the UK. There was a mission at one school where some pupils and two teachers made commitments to follow Jesus; as a consequence of this, another Scripture Union group was formed.

CMS Ireland sponsored the construction of a Youth Centre, The Kiwoko Youth Friendly Centre, in the local village. The British High Commissioner performed the opening ceremony and during the proceedings one of the teachers thanked us for starting the school's programme. She reported that fewer girls were dropping out of education because of pregnancy. This has a further significance; if a girl drops out of school prematurely, her prospects of a good marriage are reduced and her risk of contracting HIV is increased.

We were guests at the marriage of one of our staff, Dr Nicholas Lubega, to his fiancée Susan, and were impressed by the public statement they made to the effect that they had both remained virgins, saving themselves for this day. This is rather unusual, but it was witness to the fact that their faith made a radical difference in the practical area of choice. The gospel has important implications for public health.

Chapter 9

Mothers and Children

A baby is God's opinion that life should go on.
(Carl Sandburg, 1878–1967)

Uganda has the second highest fertility rate in the world, with an average of seven children per mother. This means that many women have considerably more, with associated risks to mother and child. The World Health Organisation (WHO) has estimated that, in 2003, five thousand mothers in Uganda died during pregnancy or labour. A woman in East Africa has an overall one in two hundred risk of dying from a complication of pregnancy; the comparable risk in Northern Europe is one in four thousand.

At the tenth anniversary celebration for Kiwoko Hospital, on 9 November 2001, we launched the Safe Motherhood Programme, along the lines suggested by the WHO; the goal is that no woman or child should be damaged during pregnancy or childbirth. This will require long-term education and persistence as more than half the women in rural areas are illiterate.

Husbands also need persuading, as their convenience may be threatened in the process.

Penny was seventeen. One day at school she developed severe abdominal pain and was rushed to a clinic, where she gave birth to her, ten weeks premature, baby. The school authorities informed the mother that her daughter was sick and in Kiwoko hospital but did not enlighten her as to the real situation. It was only when she arrived that she was suddenly confronted with the fact that her daughter had just given birth rather than being seriously ill. Her response was to reject Penny, for bringing such shame on her, and it took some time and to persuade her to change her mind. Even when she did so she made it clear that she would not pay any fees. The Good Samaritan Fund dealt with this aspect of the problem, and during the period of hospital treatment we were able to do some more repair work on the strained relationship. The baby was cared for in The Special Care Baby Unit (SCBU).

Harriet was a twenty-year-old woman who was brought to Kiwoko hospital one Sunday night, having had an antenatal check at another hospital, nine days previously, and been diagnosed with pre-eclampsia. This is a complication of pregnancy where there is very high blood pressure and kidney damage, so that protein leaks out in the urine. Untreated, it can progress to fits and, sometimes, death. She had refused to be admitted to the first hospital, saying she was too busy arranging her own wedding. She was thirty weeks pregnant, but the wedding arrangements were much more important to her than her own health or that of the baby. She had had a fit that Sunday at 3.00am and arrived with us, in the evening, fifteen hours later, unconscious and with an uncontrollably high blood pressure. She had a huge brain haemorrhage and fitted again. The only hope was to deliver the baby, but Harriet died on the operating table as her premature baby was being delivered by caesarean section. The baby also eventually died in our SCBU, unable to cope with the twin stresses of prematurity and the compromise to its blood supply before birth. If Harriett had been treated in time, she and the baby would almost certainly have survived. Preparation for her funeral replaced the wedding preparations: how sad, and so unnecessary.

In Uganda 70% of babies are born at home. Some babies are born to teenage mothers whose bodies have not matured sufficiently to permit a normal birth process. When labour is obstructed the baby becomes severely distressed, and will eventually die. Prolonged labour in the presence of obstruction, risks rupture of the uterus, and pressure of the baby's head can erode a hole in the bladder. Without subsequent specialised surgery the resulting urinary incontinence will be permanent, and the unfortunate woman often becomes a social outcast. Anxiety about hospital fees is the common reason for delay in seeking medical help. Old women in the village can also cause delay by advising the use of herbs to soften the bones of the pelvis and let the child out. When this fails, as it will, the young women arrive belatedly at Kiwoko hospital requiring emergency caesarean section.

Nalukwago was one such patient. Following delivery by emergency caesarean section her baby showed signs of distress and was treated for ten days in the SCBU. At first he could not even suckle, but this problem was gradually overcome and he was fit for discharge. Nalukwago owed a total of £55 but had no money to pay. Her husband, who controlled the finances, spent most of the money on alcohol, so the bills were covered by the Good Samaritan fund.

One night when I was on call, a sixteen-year-old girl was admitted with an ectopic pregnancy (when the foetus is in a fallopian tube rather than the womb). Two weeks previously, she had attended at another health centre and an incorrect diagnosis of a miscarriage had been made. Since then she had been bleeding into her abdominal cavity and had nearly died. I was astonished when she absolutely refused an operation. 'Don't you have pills I can take!' she cried. Because her condition was critical we went ahead and arranged for urgent surgery. At 11.00pm when the time came to operate, we discovered that she had run away. She was in shock from blood loss and was in danger of dying so a search party was sent out. It transpired that she was with her boyfriend's sister and he had given instructions that under no circumstances should the girl have an operation. Perhaps he was hoping that she would die as her parents were unaware of the relationship and he was a married man with other children. In addition to the social complications, he would not wish to be liable for her medical bills. Mr Sentanda, our administrator, drove half way across the district in the middle of the night, down terrible dirt roads, to obtain consent from her parents for the surgery. He returned at 2.00am, by which time we had located the girl and the surgery could proceed. Sufficient blood to fill two bottles was retrieved from her abdominal cavity and returned to her circulation; this is preferable to a transfusion, as it eliminates the risk of virus transmission. When it was all over she was glad to be alive.

Although I am not a trained surgeon I learned how to deal with these ectopic pregnancies. I came across a curious example in January 2003, a woman with bilateral ectopic pregnancies of different stages of maturity. In October she had been diagnosed as having a miscarriage and then conceived another child in December. At surgery it was clear that the original foetus was still present in one tube and the more recent one was in the other tube. I searched the Internet for other examples, without success.

We also had a case of abdominal pregnancy, a rare condition where the baby develops outside the womb; we were able to make the diagnosis at twenty-eight weeks with the help of our new ultrasound scanner. The pregnancy proceeded without significant problems and we eventually delivered a baby boy, weighing in at 1.8kg, through an abdominal incision. The placenta was attached to the inner surface of the abdominal muscles within her pelvis. The mother recovered well and was delighted, as this was the only surviving child from five pregnancies. Her husband abandoned her to avoid responsibility for the medical bill, so we covered it from The Good Samaritan Fund, and also provided her with food so that she could, in turn, provide nourishment for the baby. Around the same time we read a news report of a woman in Nottingham whose abdominal pregnancy was only diagnosed when the obstetrician set out to do a caesarean section and was astonished to find the actual situation. It gave us quite a morale boost!

Often in Uganda a midwife will see no point in trying to save a new born baby if he looks unwell, since experience has taught her that he will inevitably die (a form of self-fulfilling prophecy) and anyway, the mother can always have another child later. We have been privileged to care for many of these vulnerable little ones. By 10.00am one morning we already had three admissions of premature babies, some referred from other health units. We could not engage in high-technology medicine, which is too expensive, but trained and dedicated staff could now nurse babies in a clean environment in the SCBU.

The Special Care Baby Unit was constructed, thanks to the ISIS Foundation (a group of Bermudans). I had never done a SCBU job and was happy that Keiko Katigawa had training in this area. ISIS also sponsored Maneesh Bhatra, a paediatrician and Debbie Lester, a special care baby unit nurse from Seattle, to train staff at the hospital. Debbie stayed for a week and taught us how to care more effectively for babies who had been born prematurely or who had had a difficult birth experience. Her visit helped to reinforce a more optimistic, and realistic, approach by staff and we saw an increased number of children surviving. As she was setting up her teaching materials on her first day, a mother was admitted, having given birth on her way to hospital. Most people travel distances in shared taxis that only depart when they are fully occupied; even in emergency situations or in labour poor people have no option but to wait. The baby's umbilical cord had not been cut, and although the heart was beating he was not breathing. We managed to re-establish respiration, but two days later he died from the combination of blood loss and oxygen starvation, with consequent brain damage. However we were encouraged by the fact that he had survived for two days; it gave us hope that with a similarly intensive approach others could be saved. Next day, on the ward round, we found the mother crying; she was only fifteen years old and he had been her first baby. Pregnancy is common among adolescents; sex education is frowned upon so that young people learn from the media or by experimentation. By the age of eighteen one in every two girls has had a baby. The incidence of pregnancy is even greater; some girls are pressurised into having back-street abortions.

There have been up to ten babies in our SCBU at one time. One baby weighing only 770g, born at twenty-six weeks gestation survived for two weeks. This was another miracle, since such children have no chance of survival for even a day. In fact, under Ugandan law it is counted as a miscarriage, since babies have never survived below twenty-eight weeks. So far our record for a survivor is 800g, which we think is remarkable for a rural hospital in Uganda.

Chapter 10

A Woman's Work Is Never Done

> *A blessed thing it is for any man or woman to have a friend, one human soul whom we can trust utterly, who knows the best and worst of us, and who loves us in spite of all our faults.*
>
> (Charles Kingsley, 1819–75)

I once asked a woman how old she was when she was married. 'I was twelve years old,' she replied.

'Isn't that illegal in this country?'

'Yes, but after my parents' death I went to live with my aunt and they wanted to get rid of me and so married me off.'

'Are you happy?'

'I should be happy with a husband who looks after me.'

Her last sentence was so telling. She neither enjoyed married life nor her husband nor her children, of which she had six. She was in her mid-twenties and looked forty years old, a slave to her circumstances.

Women in rural Uganda have a very hard life. One of the women who worked for us had an unemployed husband who would take all the money she got on payday and only gave back housekeeping money when he chose to do so. The children were in rags and had neither proper clothes nor blankets. Eventually we decided to redirect some of her pay so that it could be used for the care of her children.

It is the wife's role to produce children and look after the home, rather than to be a companion. Some husbands go away to work in the city, or even go on courses abroad for years at a time, leaving their wives to cope alone at home. If she does not produce a child the husband may look for another woman to bear his children. Happily, not all marriages are like this. Some relationships are loving and committed. I remember the story of a very devoted Christian couple. 'Margaret' had had three pregnancies but had no living children. Her cervix was weak (incompetent) so that as the babies grew the cervix could not hold them back. She lost her last one, born at about twenty-six weeks and cared for in our special care baby unit (SCBU) for the few days he survived. Her husband's family had had enough and advised him to consult the witch-doctor to discover the reason. As a Christian, he would not agree to this. His other alternative was to find a 'proper' wife who could have healthy children. He refused to do this, for the same reason. During the next pregnancy a stitch was inserted in her cervix to keep it closed until the pregnancy was far advanced, and she produced a 4kg baby. It was wonderful to see the joy on her face as she held her healthy child, and to witness the stigma of childlessness lifted, and the problems with her in-laws disappear.

Women are often seen as commodities in Uganda; the man owns everything and the dowry system helps to perpetuate this. I remember reading in the agony column of *New Vision*, the Ugandan daily paper, about a woman who met a 'wonderful man', but once the dowry was paid he started to beat her. The agony columnist explained that it was because he believed that he owned her. A woman's children are also considered to be the man's property and if he dies they are passed on to his family, together with his wife's possessions. This happened to 'Florence', who was married to one of our drivers. He was very good at his job but one day, as he was driving down a fast stretch of road, he encountered a lorry pouring out black smoke. Suddenly, concealed by the smoke, another car came at high speed from the opposite direction: there was a head-on collision, resulting in the deaths of all but one of those involved. 'Florence', as well as coping with her grief, had to face the potential loss of everything to her husband's family.

I asked Ugandan Christians why the dowry still existed, and their explanation was, 'The amount I am willing to pay for my wife shows how much I love and value her.' I responded, 'Then, if you are asked to pay five cows, you should offer ten, saying, "I love her and she is worth more than that."' I cannot say that my suggestion caught on!

We found it strange when we saw the preparations for weddings. The process involves a wedding meeting at which the local community gives pledges and contributions towards the cost. Unfortunately there is an element of 'keeping up with the Joneses', as people often plan weddings far beyond their annual incomes. When Dr Anne Namugenyi, my deputy, spoke at a meeting on relationships she described some couples returning home from the wedding unable even to afford to buy sugar, and remaining in debt for many years. One of Kate's friends, whom she had met on a previous visit to Uganda, was married in church. By this stage he already had teenage children, and he was a lay reader! Only now could he afford the wedding. If this was the case for a man in his position, you can guess the difficulties for the Church in promoting marriage. Some churches have tried to solve the problem by having weddings at the regular Sunday services.

One of our roles as missionaries was to try to live out the biblical pattern of family life (by no means synonymous with the Western one!). It involved simple, but important, things like carrying one or other of our children around on my shoulders, and supporting Kate in her role as wife and mother. These activities are in themselves ordinary, but the symbolism is a challenge to a male dominated society; the worldviews of many Ugandan men within church circles are determined by tradition rather than biblical standards. A paradigm shift in this area would, perhaps, do more than any other single thing to improve the health and well-being of the women and children.

Chapter 11

The Four 'M's: Malaria, Measles, Malnutrition, Meningitis

The health of nations is more important than the wealth of nations.

(William James 'Will' Durant, 1885–1981)

Each year in Africa between 1.5 and 2.7 million children less than five years of age die of malaria. This would be like seven jumbo jets full of these children crashing every day, or the number of days in 4,100 years! Chapter 6 explained how malaria causes severe and life threatening anaemia in small children. We worry about minor problems, whereas one Ugandan child in ten does not live to see his or her first birthday.

Kiguli was eight months old and had been visiting the Kiwoko area with his mother. Their home was about 100 miles away, in Mukono on the other side of Kampala, and an area where preventive healthcare was less developed. She brought him to the hospital because he had developed a fever and thought he might have malaria. He weighed only 5kg, and had a measles rash, but she was reluctant for him to be admitted. Eventually we persuaded her, promising free treatment from the Good Samaritan Fund. It transpired that she was to be married in three days time, and she had come to make preparations; the child's illness was, therefore, a serious inconvenience. His acute illness lasted only a few days, but he was grossly malnourished and still needed a lot of support. When the father, and prospective bridegroom, arrived, he was most annoyed at the situation. 'How dare this child interfere with his wedding! What sort of woman was this, producing a sick child! If he died, so what? There would be other children in the future ...' There was no possibility of reasoning with him and there was a distinct possibility that he would use physical violence, so we had no option but to let them all leave. They promised to take Kiguli to a nearby clinic for monitoring, but I had no confidence that they would. I felt pity for the mother, joined to a man like that. It is another example of how poverty puts pressure on women. I remember asking a man, 'How many other children do you have?' He stood and thought for a while, but then had to ask his wife!

We rarely see measles in our district now, following an intensive measles immunisation programme. This was prompted by a measles scare and lifted the prevalence of immunisation from 50% to 85% over a period of five years, higher than in some parts of the UK. I am amazed at complacency about measles in the UK. People seem to have forgotten that it is a killer disease; it still causes 5% of all deaths in children in the developing world. The reason for its virulence is twofold: it causes illness in its own right, including inflammation of the brain; the virus also depresses the immune system, so that children are at risk of secondary infections. Immunising a high proportion of children in an area, thus building up 'herd immunity', will prevent an epidemic. As a consequence of the programme there was a 75% reduction in mortality of children living in our local area, whereas there was no improvement in more remote areas. It was so obvious that, when we were about to leave, local people thanked us for the fact that their children were not dying any more.

It is difficult for Westerners to appreciate what it means to be really hungry. We are used to eating three meals a day, except when we choose to diet. For two-thirds of the world hunger is a lifestyle, not just a bit of discomfort before lunch. I discovered that when a patient did not have an attendant and was going hungry, our nurses would share their evening meal with him; they and their children would have less to eat that day. It made me feel rather ashamed. The nurses were obeying the very words of Jesus, at personal cost, while we were eating well.

It is salutary for us to consider some facts about nutrition. Parts of this chapter are inspired by the chapter 'State of the World Need' by the World Relief Corporation in *Perspectives on the World Christian Movement*, 3rd edition, edited by Ralph Winter and Steven Hawthorne (Paternoster, Carlisle, 1999), ch. 81.

- Three quarters of a billion people in the world are chronically undernourished.
- Malnutrition is the underlying cause of 55% of deaths of children under five years;
- Malnutrition is the direct cause in 10% of these deaths.
- Worldwide, 34,000 children die every day of hunger and preventable diseases, twenty-four every minute of every day.
- Basic health care including nutrition would cost $13 billion per year.
- In the USA $30/50 billion is spent every year on diets and to reduce calorie intake, $28 billion on pizzas, and $17 billion on pet foods.
- In the UK £100 million is spent on Christmas presents for pets.

Kate once overheard a conversation at a butcher's shop in Kampala; an expatriate woman was buying some meat. 'It doesn't have to be too good; it's only for my dog.' She didn't seem to realise that, for the person serving her, meat was probably a luxury food.

A girl called Annet Namugga was admitted, suffering from kwashiorkor. In this condition the child's abdomen becomes very swollen as a result of eating a diet consisting almost entirely of carbohydrate foods with low nutritional value, such as maize flour or cassava. Europeans consider that cassava looks and tastes like putty, but it is the staple diet for many Ugandans. There are two additional health hazards with cassava. I have heard that it contains cyanide, which persists unless the food is cooked sufficiently. A well-nourished body can remove the cyanide by means of an enzyme, but malnourished people cannot manufacture this enzyme and are, therefore, in danger of being poisoned. Secondly, there is some evidence that cassava can cause endomyocardial fibrosis, i.e. serious damage to heart muscle. Women suffer from this more often because they eat the raw cassava while they are cooking. It may also be linked with toxicity with the rare metal cerium.

On casual inspection Annet, with her rotund abdomen, appeared well nourished, but she had severe protein deficiency and her appearance was due to an excess of fluid in her body. Treatment consisted of feeding with food rich in protein. Gradually she eliminated the excess fluid and it became apparent that she weighed only 4kg, typical of an infant, rather than a four-year-old child. It is not surprising that there is a 30% risk of death in such severely malnourished children. It gradually became clear that she was mentally handicapped; this could either have been the consequence of chronic malnutrition or the reason why she was neglected in the first place. Her guardians had left a false address, having brought Annet to the hospital and dumped her. We adopted her and she continued to live on the ward until we found a local woman who was willing to foster her. We paid for her food and clothes and fees for the local school, but it was still a big task for the foster mother to care for such a neglected and mentally handicapped child.

We needed wisdom in managing situations like this; the hospital could easily have turned into a children's home and been diverted from its primary calling as a place of healing. The New Hope Uganda Children's Home, set up by Jay and Vicky Dangers, provided a partial solution. Matt and Julie Shorack were working there and had built a home for babies. They were able to offer a place to Nalukwago, a five-month-old baby, whose mother had died during the birth process; her father did not know how to look after her and she had not been vaccinated. She was grossly underweight and very, very sick, having had fever for a week and convulsions for three days, during which time she had also been unconscious. A lumbar puncture confirmed meningitis, now at an advanced stage. The delay in coming to hospital was because the family had persevered with traditional remedies; now they had given up hope and abandoned her. She recovered from the infection but was left with severe brain damage and we were left with the problem of her long-term care. Our friends at New Hope stepped in and adopted her, so that Nalukwago could at last receive love and care. Initially she seemed to respond and they gave her the name Hope. However, after just a week in her new home she stopped breathing and was rushed back to Kiwoko. We could not save her life but it was some consolation that in the last few weeks of her all too short life, she had been shown love and affection, as befits one of God's precious creatures.

Frank was a handsome six-year-old boy. He came to Kiwoko about ten months previously with severe meningitis. Probably the family had delayed in the village due to lack of finances. After a full course of treatment he improved dramatically but he too had permanent brain damage. His mother, who was at the hospital attending to his needs, had separated from Frank's father and there was no financial support; she was also pregnant. One day, after delivering her baby she left the hospital, abandoning Frank and leaving the hospital fully responsible for his future. Although he had severe brain damage he was still a human being in need of human relationships; he could sense when someone was near, he would cry when he was hungry. He was given a room of his own in the isolation part of the paediatric ward. The nurses bathed him, fed him and tucked him up in bed, and he became a special favourite. He had a specially made chair to help with his physiotherapy and he sat outside in the sunshine, watching the world go by. Passers-by smiled at him. Despite all the care and attention from many devoted staff his condition deteriorated, his breathing became laboured, and finally he passed away. Without Frank there was a sense of something, or someone, missing.

The parents were informed but we were told that they had separated and were not interested. Frank had become part of our family, so we held a funeral service and buried him at the hospital farm. Our administrator commented that Frank had probably received more care during the last few days of his life than at any other time. Frank taught us the value of a human life, however little that life would appear to have achieved in worldly terms.

Chapter 12

We Treat, Jesus Heals

> *If there is light in the soul, there will be beauty in the person. If there is beauty in the person, there will be harmony in the house. If there is harmony in the house, there will be order in the nation. If there is order in the nation, there will be peace in the world.*
>
> (Chinese proverb)

Our motto is: 'We treat, Jesus heals'. The goal is healing of the whole person, body, mind, and spirit. Health is not merely the absence of disease but includes an overall sense of physical, mental, social and spiritual well-being.

Christmas is usually a time for drunken fights and road accidents. The pre-Christmas period in 2000 was particularly violent as it coincided with the run-up to the presidential elections, and there was an atmosphere of fear in the local district. A policeman was ambushed in Luwero Town, and shot through the stomach. His survival owed much to the skill and determination of Dr Nicholas, who spent five hours in the operating theatre with him. On 22 December, at around 10.00am, I was completing my round on the maternity ward when an urgent message arrived. Terrorists had driven into Kiwoko village, burned down the police post, shot a policewoman, and hijacked our farm vehicle. The vehicle, abandoned in the bush, was retrieved later that day. After delivering a baby by caesarean section at midnight on Christmas Day, my next patient was one I had met just a week before when her niece, Jackie, one of our medical record officers married. She arrived with a gunshot wound in her leg. Thankfully the bullet had not caused any serious damage.

Violence was prevalent during the election campaign and many bombs were exploded when President Museveni's re-election was announced. A number of our staff had a close shave with one of them. They had travelled to Kampala in the hospital minibus to buy some drugs, and it broke down on arrival in the city. For the whole day they tried to have it repaired without success. At 7.00pm they gave up and hired a taxi from the Kampala Taxi Park and returned to Kiwoko. At 7.10pm a bomb exploded close to where the taxi had been, and a woman was killed.

There were also frequent ambushes of vehicles late at night. Near Luwero, our nearest town, five thieves stopped a minibus taxi, stole all the valuables, and stripped everyone naked. They kidnapped two school-girls before making off. Amazingly the girls were released the following day.

One hot sunny afternoon another taxi was waiting. It would not leave until every seat was filled, so the passengers waited in silence. At last a young man arrived carrying a boy of about four years, mother followed close behind with another child on her back. What a relief! Here were the long-awaited passengers. The boy screamed in pain as he was lifted into the taxi. His left leg was swollen and foul smelling. It was apparent that he was very ill and the other passengers felt sorry for him. We discovered that his name was Dudu, and that he was from the Nkore tribe, who come from Western Uganda. Karamajong cattle rustlers, from Northern Uganda, had stolen all their cattle and had murdered his father about three weeks previously. His mother had been left destitute with three young children to support, Dudu being the eldest. He had developed a swelling on his left leg about two weeks previously, and it had not improved on treatment with traditional herbs. They had travelled to Nakasongola police station, about fifty miles away and were referred to Kiwoko hospital. The mother only had enough money to pay for transport. The taxi brought them to Kiwoko and we covered Dudu's fees and their living expenses from the Good Samaritan Fund. He had non-Hodgkin's lymphoma (a cancer of the lymph nodes) and following consultation with our visiting orthopaedic surgeon, his left leg was amputated. This relieved his pain, and his smile returned. Even with a significant disability he has hope for the future.

Namutebi was an eleven-year-old girl with a rather shy smile. She had been admitted with an abdominal swelling and, following a biopsy, a diagnosis of Burkitt's lymphoma (a common cancer in Uganda) was made.

Chemotherapy usually brings about a permanent cure, and she began to improve. Her mother at first stayed with her at the hospital but she left one day after getting bad news. She went home leaving Namutebi in the care of another patient's family. On her return we found out her father had been murdered in his village. There was no trace of the murderers and the motive was unknown. Namutebi's mother had gone home to attend the burial. On her return she recounted the sad story. Her grief was not just at the loss of her father, she had also lost a valuable source of financial help. Namutebi has had further courses of chemotherapy and it is probable that she will be cured, a light in the darkness.

Sometimes people would abandon hope of saving life. On one occasion I was wakened to attend to an asthmatic patient who had nearly died during a previous admission. As I rushed to see him, I was informed that a child had just arrived, suffering from meningitis. Whose need was most urgent? I decided on the man and as soon as I saw him I realised that he was on the point of death. A few moments later he stopped breathing and his heart stopped. 'He's dead,' said the relatives, and rose to leave. 'Not yet!' I replied, since the adrenaline injection had just arrived. Following this and some heart massage and he started breathing again, and three hours later he awoke from his unconscious state. He was a good member of his church and on our Hospital Board, but his first response was to repent of his sins. Perhaps, while technically dead, he had experienced something that made him realise his need of salvation. A week later he still could not believe that he was alive. Thanks are most due to our wonderful nurses, without them he would probably have remained dead!

In Uganda, mental illness is commonly attributed to evil spirits and curses. Cure requires either the services of a witch-doctor or some powerful injections. We treated one mentally disturbed boy who gradually recovered and remained well with only oral medication. His mother was so impressed that she decided to become a Christian!

Sometimes we cannot cure an illness but we can still hold out the hope of eternal life. Abdul was a Muslim who was admitted one December with an abdominal mass. At surgery it turned out to be a rare cancer, which was untreatable. When he subsequently returned to inquire if anything could be done about the expanding mass in his abdomen, I had to tell him again that he had cancer and that he would die that year. He needed to make his peace with God. Our chaplain visited him and he made a commitment to Christ. It turned out that he had been a churchgoer but he had become disillusioned with the dead religion in his church so had become a Muslim, and had changed his name. Now he wanted his old name again, George William!

Chapter 13

Magic and Mismanagement

> Be careful of reading health books, you might die of
> a misprint.
> (Mark Twain, 1835–1910)

In all countries and cultures alternative practitioners offer a variety of possible solutions to sickness. In Uganda these range from traditional healers and witch-doctors to untrained health practitioners. The rural population has no means to distinguish between a qualified doctor and a village health worker; in the local language they are all called *basawo*, a term embracing any kind of practitioner; a traditional healer is also a *basawo*. There is no quality control; anyone can set up a clinic and offer services they have no training or competence to provide. Sometimes this causes a critical delay in receiving suitable care. It frequently makes the original illness significantly worse, sometimes with fatal results.

Kiwoko village had one such 'health' clinic. The practitioner would often refer patients to us when at death's door. This would avoid a bad reputation as a result of death on his premises. We often had to pick up the pieces of repeated disasters. Fifteen patients had their jaws broken during dental extractions. One man had been unconscious for five days, he had no fever but nevertheless they gave him quinine injections for cerebral malaria and also antibiotics. He recovered rapidly when we treated his diabetic coma. He was the second person to come to us with the same condition, from the same clinic, that week. Many people in the villages are unaware that there are causes of coma apart from malaria, and this ignorance probably results in many unnecessary deaths. We were astonished that anyone would choose to attend such a clinic knowing that there was a good hospital nearby. They had no licence to practise, but no effort was made to close the clinic down. I wonder if perhaps money might have something to do with the status quo, perhaps even a little to do with bribery. Patients made the choice purely on the grounds of cost, but what a false economy. It is so important that local people know that our doors are open and they will not be refused treatment if they genuinely cannot afford it.

The community work of Kiwoko hospital mainly concentrated on immunisation clinics. One of my first priorities after taking charge was to visit the village areas and make an assessment of this programme. One day I went to a village and from a distance I saw an extra-ordinary sight, a very strange looking child with half his face black and the other half brown. To complete the unusual appearance he had a red lump on his forehead.

On closer inspection it became apparent that the red lump was not the growth I had been expecting but a tomato tied to his head; the brown half of his face was caked with earth. This strange sight turned out to be the local treatment for an eye infection, most probably trachoma. This is one of the leading causes of blindness in the developing world, easily treated with antibiotics and good hygiene. The family's faith in the traditional remedy was unshakable and they would not bring him to hospital. They also claimed not to have any money, despite the fact that they were building a brick house and I could see new iron sheets on the roof. We sent them some antibiotics anyway and eventually they relented and brought the child to Kiwoko with his sight intact. What a shame if he had lost his sight through ignorance and false economy.

Cattle herders in Uganda lead nomadic lifestyles, in rural and often swampy settings; being uneducated, their health care needs are often ignored, and they use traditional remedies. We started a clinic in a place called Ngoma, fifty miles away, in order to reach out to them. We encountered a three-month-old child who had attended a local clinic because of a febrile convulsion. The appropriate procedure is to cool the child and test for malaria and meningitis. The clinic had adopted a more radical approach and burned the child all over his back. There were now two problems – burns as well as the cause of the fever. The lumbar puncture was clear, the fit was due to a fever associated with otherwise uncomplicated malaria, from which he made a complete recovery. The burn scars will remain for life.

I saw another child with burns all around his head. When I asked the mother what had happened she explained that people in the village had advised her that his head was the wrong shape, and this was considered to be the appropriate treatment. In the UK situations like these would be regarded as serious child abuse, probably resulting in the children being taken into care. In Uganda, with so much illiteracy and with entrenched beliefs in witch-doctors, there is no pressure for such intervention. The powerful triad of poverty, ignorance and traditional beliefs conspire to impose much misery and suffering.

The undercurrent of witchcraft is revealed when enquiring as to a child's immunisation status. We would say, 'Has she been immunised?' In Luganda one says, 'Have they (the outside forces) immunised her?' Many Ugandans believe that external forces control the physical world. In the face of trouble most Ugandans still rely on the traditional healer (witch-doctor) for help. It is considered very important to determine the cause of misfortune. It may be that a curse has been placed on a person. He may have offended the ancestors who are now striking back. The witch-doctor's advice (divination) is a path of discovery and also a way to seek redress.

When Ian Clarke carried out a survey of beliefs about AIDS, he found that there were believed to be two sorts of AIDS; one was due to the HIV virus; the other was caused by witchcraft. Infertility is a common problem in Uganda. A visit to the traditional healer sometimes 'cured' the problem, by having intercourse with him! It has been reported that one 'healer' advised a man with HIV to have sex with a three-year-old girl as a means of effecting a cure, or at least of diluting the level of the virus in his body. Defilement, as this is called, seems to be a very common practice. It carries a very stiff jail sentence and possibly the death penalty, but sometimes cases are settled out of court by payment to the child's parents. This kind of talk about herbalists and traditional healers may not be politically correct, but we need to face facts. As Christians we also believe in the invisible world of good and evil, but we also believe in God as the Sovereign of the whole created universe.

> 'The one who is in you is greater than the one who is in the world.'

> (1 John 4:4)

Illiteracy is a major problem in Uganda. Under these circumstances it is difficult to separate truth from falsehood. In some areas more than 50% of women are unable to read or write. Education targeting girls and women is vitally important because they are the keystones of their families. A charismatic personality can easily gather followers where there is ignorance. One cult, located about four miles from Kiwoko, was led by a man who claimed that he would die and rise again in June 1999. The appointed time came and went without incident but then people began to come to the hospital with children suffering from measles. So many that it amounted to an epidemic. The children had not been immunised, there was no point since the world was about to end. I asked one man what he thought of the cult. 'We have been deceived,' he replied, as he nursed his child seriously ill with measles, a potentially fatal disease.

There were other tragic consequences. People, already poor, had handed over most of their possessions to the cult. There were also stories of sexual abuse and a possible human sacrifice and many people died. The Government shut the camp but, unfortunately, the leader escaped.

Another cult leader, Joseph Kibwetere, was a lapsed Catholic with a history of mental illness. He gathered followers and predicted that the world would end at a certain date in 2000. In anticipation of this he corralled them in a church building in Kanungu and set it on fire. Those who were not totally consumed in this inferno were later found buried beneath some buildings belonging to the cult. Possibly they had been murdered when they tried to leave.

Even those with more orthodox Christian beliefs are not immune to deception. Some believed that the world would end at the Millennium and religious leaders instructed their people to be in prayer meetings on 31 December 1999. In one situation children were made to fast and were denied food and water, and some died. The leaders were arrested. Incidents such as these have brought the Christian faith into disrepute. Stories like these indicate how much people need to be instructed in the Bible and have support from wise and caring pastors. This is happening in many churches and we had the privilege of meeting amazing and committed Christians who put us to shame with their prayer life, fasting and zeal for evangelism.

Chapter 14

Landmarks

> *The history of every country begins in the heart of a man or woman.*
> (Willa Sibert Cather, 1873–1947)

The most important official event during our six years at Kiwoko was the tenth anniversary of the formal opening of the hospital on 9 November 1991. Ian Clarke had worked at Kiwoko from 1988 and had begun to build the first structures, but the official opening, by the then Vice-President of Uganda, the late Dr Samson Kisekka, did not take place until September 1991. The Minister of Health, Brigadier the Hon. Jim Muhwezi, MP, was the Guest of Honour at this tenth anniversary. He had spent five years as a soldier fighting during the war of the 1980s and was delighted to be back in Kiwoko under wonderfully different circumstances. He recalled that the area had been so devastated during the war that none of the roads through the bush were visible. People were dying every week from snakebites as Luwero District had returned to bush with snakes everywhere. The pews in the local church had been burned for firewood; the roof survived only because the church was commandeered as the army barracks. Our guests were astonished at the rapid growth of the hospital from such humble beginnings, and were appreciative of the associated development in the whole surrounding area.

The founder members of the Kiwoko Hospital staff are known as 'The Historicals'; they had joined the staff when Luwero was a difficult place in which to live and work, and had been very faithful over the intervening years. We gave them a place of honour at the ceremony and awarded them certificates of long service. We, as relative newcomers, can easily overlook the struggles of the pioneers. As we celebrated in the midst of the large modern campus it would have been easy to conclude that shortage of money was never an issue, but that is far from the truth. I asked some of the Historicals to recall that era. For instance, in Richard Montgomery's time paper was a luxury item and medical notes had to be written in tiny script on a single piece of paper. Margaret Kacence, now deputy matron, began her career as an enrolled nurse. She recalled how adult men would arrive for treatment wearing only a pair of underpants and a coat, as they had no other clothes. The Minister of Health was very surprised to see Margaret in Kiwoko; they had grown up together and had been classmates at school!

Every year in Uganda there is a government spon- sored surgical camp, during which senior consultants in different branches of surgery come and operate on patients with challenging conditions. It circulates around the various districts. When a new building is to be opened it is our practise to invite various dignitaries to share in the occasion; this has helped to establish links between the Ugandan Government and overseas donors. When the new operating theatre was completed we invited the Minister of State for Health, the Hon. Mike Mukula, to perform the opening ceremony and he was so impressed with the facilities that he promised to locate the surgical camp at Kiwoko Hospital that year.

The original intention had been to hold the camp in Northern Uganda, but that region had become dangerous and unstable. This resulted from the activities of what is termed The Lord's Resistance Army, led by Joseph Kony. His stated ambition is to re-establish the Ten Commandments, but his movement is, in reality, an evil concoction of pseudo-religious, pagan and occult beliefs. All sorts of atrocities are committed, including kidnapping young girls as concubines for their fighters and using young boys and girls as soldiers. There have been horrific reports of murder and intimidation of the population of northern Uganda, in the territory of the Acholi tribe.

The surgical camp was, therefore, moved to Central Uganda, to the Luwero District. It had always previously been located at Government hospitals but, since Kiwoko Hospital now had such good facilities with the inauguration of the new theatres, we were selected to host the event in June 2003. It was a great honour for the hospital and we were thrilled that we were able act as hosts. The First Lady, Mrs Janet Museveni, opened the camp. She thanked Kiwoko Hospital for its services and commented on the great developments, such as the Special Care Baby Unit, that were bringing healing to needy people who would not otherwise have survived. Her first visit to us had been informal, but now, in the post-9/11 world, security was so tight that our children, Ben and Anna, were just about allowed to present her with flowers, but we were not allowed to have our cameras; however, the official Uganda TV cameraman gave us a copy of the video. The other guest of honour, who closed the camp, was the Nnabagereka of Buganda. She is the local Queen and attracts huge crowds just as Princess Diana used to do on her travels.

The surgeons donated their time and expertise free of charge, to the great benefit of the local population, but the hospital incurred considerable expense. This was covered by donations from Friends of Kiwoko Hospital. It was amazing to see five operations proceeding simultaneously in the two theatres, a major one in the main theatre, two in the minor theatre, and two more in the corridor! Western surgeons might be horrified about the risk of wound infections but this was the only opportunity for poor people to have much needed surgery. Unfortunately some did get infections, since some of the patients of course had undiagnosed HIV. It was also good publicity for the hospital, which was featured in the local papers nearly every day for more than a week. It generated much goodwill and help with future developments in partnership with Government we hope will involve us training community doctors.

For this we would need to provide residential accommodation at the hospital and teaching both there and in the surrounding district. It was encouraging to see that a work that had started in such a humble fashion has now become highly respected throughout the country. Do not despise small things.

Whenever we erected a new building the joke circulated that I would then take a special interest in that particular area. When the new theatre was built someone suggested that I might now try and complete my surgical training. They considered me to be almost proficient now in obstetrics, capable of performing a caesarean section in less than twenty minutes. However, it was a different story with general surgery. The Ugandan staff would shake their heads, 'A novice still!'

Chapter 15

Education

> *From what we get, we can make a living; what we give,*
> *however, makes a life.*
> (Arthur Ashe, 1943–93)

AIDS causes disease, suffering and poverty. It also leaves orphans, children who are sometimes at the mercy of unscrupulous people. How are they to support themselves without resources? How are they to live?

One key to the solution is the provision of education for girls. It opens the door to a career and they no longer need to look for a sugar daddy to supply their basic needs. Girls who give sexual favours in order to survive are at risk of HIV infection. One of Ian Clarke's motives in initiating the nurse-aide and laboratory training schools was to provide a way out of the poverty trap and create worthwhile employment for local young people. He also needed to train local staff because qualified nurses from other districts would not come to an area that had been devastated by war. We now train enrolled comprehensive nurses, a much higher level than nurse-aids. One year three of the top four laboratory-assistant students in Uganda, were from the Kiwoko Training School. The Ministry of Health regards Kiwoko Hospital as a key contributor to nurse training in Uganda. It is the only nurse training school in the whole area between Kampala in the south and Gulu in the north, more than 200 miles apart. This is a measure of how much the hospital has developed since its formal opening in September 1991. Many of the former students take the vision and values of the hospital with them to other parts of the country.

On another occasion we raised enough money to fund five orphans to attend training schools. Orphans are underprivileged and have few opportunities to improve themselves. Sadly only three passed interviews to see if they could cope with the courses. Two of those three were able to commence training to be nurses and in due course will be able to support other family members who in turn can receive education and obtain employment. The third was found to be pregnant and was unable to participate; the cycle of being under-privileged continued and she may subsequently put herself at risk of AIDS and an early death, leaving another orphan.

Harriet and John are good examples of the benefits of this approach. Their parents died of AIDS leaving them and their other children orphans. Harriet joined the basic pharmacy-aide course, designed to provide a career for young people in her situation. Her subsequent employment enabled her to finance two of her siblings to attend school. When John was left to fend for himself after becoming orphaned at the age of fourteen his school fees were paid by the local council. He joined the Nurse Training School wanting a career that would benefit his whole family. His O-level grades were poor, which is not surprising given his background, but he seized his opportunity with both hands and turned out to be one of our best students. A far cry from England where we take education for granted.

We also started a tailoring school to train other orphans in practical skills so that they can earn their living as village tailors. There were twenty-two of them and thanks to one generous donor we were able to provide every one of them with a sewing machine and to employ a tailor to teach them. Some of those from the tailoring school were subsequently able to afford to go back to school and thus open up other possibilities for employment.

As I look back at my time at Kiwoko, I wonder, 'Where did I make the most difference?' The area that most readily comes to mind is orphan sponsorship, much of it funded by Compassion Canada and a variety of AIDS charities. I think of people employed as tailors, nurses, and laboratory or pharmacy aides, with a future and a hope instead of living hand to mouth. Part of the sadness of the situation is that we cannot help everyone but we can make a real difference and give hope to many.

Exam results can be overemphasised; school grades do not guarantee that good doctors and nurses will result at the end of training. We were informed in 2002 that our current student nurses would have to meet strict O-level requirements and it seemed that a spanner had been thrown into the works, sufficient to bring the school to a dead stop. Imagine for a moment this scenario – you are an orphan, malnourished and struggling to survive, and attending a school in the bush where some O-levels are not even taught. How do you think you would fare? These young women lacked opportunity, not intelligence, but the Ugandan Nurses Council instructed us to discharge all those who did not have certificates in O-level science. This ruling had never previously been enforced and was unfair to the rural poor who make up 80% of the rural population.

This led to a year-long battle. It flew in the face of natural justice to the poor so we refused to comply; it would have rendered them vulnerable to sugar daddies in order to survive. And who would take their places? It would not be richer girls, who had educational advantages and were thus able to obtain better grades; they would continue to opt for university courses rather than careers in nursing. They would certainly not choose to work in Northern or Central Uganda, where there is poverty or civil unrest, or both.

In the end I wrote to the First Lady, Mrs Museveni, whom I knew to be a supporter of the rural poor, especially the women. She referred me to the Minister of Health and, when they attended the opening of the surgical camp together, they ruled that students should not be sent away; they would be accredited if they passed the Nursing Council exams.

Having invested time and resources into training nurses, and instilling our values into them, it is difficult to see them go and then have to start all over again, but this is part of life. We were impressed by the need to train people as disciples, not just impart medical knowledge and teach practical skills. We want them to take away Christian values from the ethos of the hospital and be salt and light wherever they subsequently go, making further disciples.

We considered it a top priority to look after our staff and take an interest in their welfare. It had an important spin off; when we were committed to them, they became committed to us. Kiwoko is in an isolated rural setting, far from the facilities of the city but we should still pay competitive wages and provide good accommodation. Some of our qualified nurses had to share rooms, as if they were still students, so we embarked on a building programme to provide suitable accommodation for them and many single occupancy units have now been constructed.

In 2001–02 we lost some staff to government hospitals, where staff salaries were increased even though there was not enough money to buy necessary drugs. We increased nurses' pay by 20% but this did not prove a sufficient incentive; government employment involved less work and held out the possibility of opening private clinics and earning more money. People like to work in Kiwoko as they enjoy the job satisfaction, but many struggle. Members of their extended families come with their various needs and often advise the staff to get better paid jobs elsewhere.

Commitment to staff also involves sponsoring them to take specialist courses and these can be very expensive, typically about £1,000 for a nurse and £5,000 for a doctor. Staff are given the opportunity to train and advance their careers, in return for a commitment to work in the hospital for an agreed subsequent period. This is difficult to fund in a resource-poor environment, and is one of the areas that Jim McAnlis, appointed as programmes director in 2003, is addressing. There is no doubt that accommodation and sponsorship are two key areas for future development.

Incidents when we have had patients requiring complex surgery have emphasised the need to have a trained surgeon on site. It is difficult to attract missionaries to work in the bush and this is also the case with Ugandan doctors who can earn much more working in private practice in Kampala. We decided that the best way to deal with this problem was to sponsor a suitable doctor to train in surgery, with a commitment to work at Kiwoko for several years afterwards, while the next one is being similarly trained. We encouraged and part-sponsored Peter Sserwadda to train in surgery and he is now our resident surgeon and acting medical superintendent. Kiwoko has a high reputation in medical circles in Uganda so time spent working here strengthens a surgeon's reputation.

We are blessed to have young doctors like Peter and James Nnyonyintono, a surgeon and previous acting medical superintendent, who combine high professional standards with strong faith. Nurses have also undertaken specialist training. Maureen Katefureeka is a registered nurse who upgraded to become an anaesthetic officer and is also a very valuable asset to the hospital.

Chapter 16

Power to Live By

> *The wise man in the storm prays God, not for safety from danger, but for deliverance from fear.*
> (Ralph Waldo Emerson, 1803–82)

One of the Friends of Kiwoko Hospital told me of the time he used to revise for important exams by candle-light because of frequent electricity power cuts during the Ulster workers' strike in 1974. Kiwoko began without the luxury of any electricity. Then we obtained a generator, but it was expensive to operate. Eventually we were connected to the grid, but power cuts often occurred. The back-up generator would come on from 7.00pm to 9.30pm so that the nurses could check the patients' pulses and blood pressures etc., but it was then promptly switched off. The person responsible for this did not necessarily have any appreciation of what was going on in the rest of the hospital. One evening I was carrying out a caesarean section, difficult enough for me even in a well-lit room. I had just lifted the baby out of the abdomen and was in the process of handing it over to a nurse, when the power went off. Yes, it was 9.30pm precisely, and we were several hours into a power cut. I was left holding the baby in pitch darkness. The mother lay on the table and the placenta had yet to be delivered. A nurse went running off to find the security guard who was in charge of switching the generator on and off.

'But it is to be switched off at half-past nine exactly. I have been told this, I have it in writing.'

'But Doctor Nick is performing an operation!'

'But nobody told me, I was only doing my duty.'

You can imagine the conversation. After what seemed an eternity a nurse ran in with a torch. I handed the baby over and closed the wound; power was restored before we finished the whole procedure. On a subsequent occasion, I carried out a caesarean section from start to finish by the light of two torches; amazingly neither mother nor baby came to any harm. We changed the rule; the generator should not be switched off until the guard had checked that theatre was not in use. We realised, in retrospect, that common sense requires simple communication and rules need to be clearly written.

I could control neither the Ugandan Electricity Board nor the weather that brought down our power lines at about 4.30pm on Sunday 21 May 2000. Kiwoko experienced a hurricane that destroyed buildings, uprooted trees and decimated crops, the hospital included. Afterwards the scene resembled a battle zone and three important buildings were badly damaged. Many trees were blown down, one landing on a hospital farm vehicle, without damaging it. The roof of the generator house was ripped off and the generator was flooded. Thankfully no one was injured in any of the affected areas.

One of the student nurses' hostels had the whole roof blown off, leaving bent and useless iron roofing sheets scattered all around. The gable end had collapsed and the contents of the hostel were soaked. Thankfully very few students were there at the time so no one was injured, although one student had to be sedated for shock. About thirty students spent the next night sleeping in the classrooms. It was only a week since the new first-year student intake had arrived and already they had had to cope with this. The other two buildings were the outpatient block and the new male ward. In each case half the roof had been removed. We managed to move the patients to the other half of the ward.

All the power lines were down and we did not expect mains power to be restored for many weeks. This made the hospital totally dependent on the generator for power, but we could not afford to keep the generator working continuously. It cost nearly £350 per week to pump water for twelve hours a day, and rising fuel prices made matters worse. It was, therefore, a difficult time but the staff rose to the occasion and we came through the crisis. Within two days most of the serious damage had been repaired, thanks to the efforts of Garry Ion (CMS) and his team of builders, who worked flat out in very hot weather. By 7 June all the repairs had been carried out and existing buildings were strengthened during the next few weeks. The repairs cost nearly £2,500. We had the money in our reserves, but it had been earmarked to cover anticipated deficits from fees during the long dry summer season. Our spirits rose when we received a gift from an overseas church almost sufficient to cover the costs of repairs. Following this we investigated insurance cover against future disasters, but found it prohibitively expensive.

While the hospital suffered relatively lightly, the centre of the storm was Kiwoko village, which now lay in ruins. The Anglican school had been severely damaged and another local school had been reduced to rubble. Consequently education suffered, threatening future development. Many people had only enough money for food and could not afford to repair what had already been substandard accommodation. There was no money left for hospital fees or other emergencies. Garry wrote in an e-mail: 'Please remember Kiwoko in your prayers, both the hospital and the local community. The people here are very resilient but life is tough and money very scarce.' The hospital was able to help by donating some damaged but usable iron sheets to local people for use in their rebuilding work.

One answer to sudden power failures is solar power; this involved looking for a donor. When Dr Keiko Katigawa joined us from Japan, she was able to develop links with the Japanese Embassy, which offered to consider funding the project. Rory Alec visited with the God Channel, a Christian satellite TV station, in November 2001; they offered to build a new operating theatre. The Kiwoko solar project powered light to all the wards and to the new theatre. It was wonderful to walk through the wards during 'power on', and see the nurses at work using the solar lighting. Solar would automatically come on during power cuts in theatre, so it made it so much easier to properly attend to the patients' needs and Kiwoko became a pioneer hospital in Uganda for this area of technology.

Chapter 17

VIPs

> *A noble person attracts noble people, and knows how to hold on to them.*
> (Johann Wolfgang von Goethe, 1749–1832)

We would often invite a VIP to open new buildings, partly as a way of networking with the Ugandan Government, but also because we know they have a genuine interest in the work. Following Mrs Museveni's first visit in 1999 there was increased recognition of our contribution to the health service and we started getting more government money towards our expenses. We were pleased about this because we are a Ugandan hospital and exist to serve the country and community. We have on various occasions invited representatives of the Ugandan Ministry of Health, as we wanted them to know how we were using their money (10–15% of the running costs of the hospital come from this source). The British High Commission has also been a stalwart supporter so every two years when each new High Commissioner was installed we invited him to visit Kiwoko.

VIP visitors of many sorts came during my time as medical superintendent. The first arrived, unannounced, on 31 December 1997, the very same day I was invited to become medical superintendent by the Bishop of Luwero who had called me to his office to discuss the appointment. Hot foot from the meeting we arrived back in the hospital to find an Irish contingent milling around, looking at us curiously, and enquiring who else we knew. The reason for this sudden surge of interest became clear when Lord Mayhew, the former Attorney General and Secretary of State for Northern Ireland appeared. Kiwoko hospital had been initiated from Northern Ireland, so that there was already an obvious connection but we seemed to be receiving the credit for the unexpected visit. We discovered that Kiwoko had not been the original destination. He was part of a group going to Murchison Falls, five hours north of us, together with his son Barney, who I had known at Oxford and who was now working in Rwanda. Their car had broken down near the turn off to the hospital, resulting in their unscheduled arrival. So I wasn't as influential as everyone had assumed!

Apart from eating House of Lords chocolates, the most memorable part of this experience was taking Lord and Lady Mayhew on a tour that ended at Rose Cottage, where Billy Barclay, the Northern Irish engineer lived. In fact Kiwoko had had three engineers from Northern Ireland, oddly enough all called Billy. The story is still told of one of the other Billys talking to Richard Montgomery, the second medical superintendent. Some of the Ugandan staff listened to the conversation. Now

Billy had an accent so broad that it was incomprehensible to the average Ugandan. They were amazed that Billy and Richard could have a conversation, as Richard was talking in English and Billy was apparently talking in a strange, unknown, language. Remarkably, Billy understood everything Richard said but replied in his own language. For his part Richard understood Billy but could not speak the foreign tongue. I am not sure if anyone ever explained that the two languages were actually one and the same. It reminds me of what happened to two Irish staff when they went to Kampala for lessons in Luganda, They were quickly dismissed and told to come back when they had learned to speak English.

On arrival at Rose Cottage with Lord Mayhew, Billy, fresh from the shower, emerged wearing the smallest towel imaginable. As a former soldier in Northern Ireland, he was overjoyed to see the previous Secretary of State. 'Sir Patrick, I am happy to see you!' he said, gesticulating wildly and emerging through the doorway. A crowd was gathering and an accident was waiting to happen so, with all the authority of my new position, I suggested that he exchanged his fig leaf for something more substantial. At morning prayers next day, I tried to play down the situation by saying that my friend Barney had come with his parents but Donald Brownlie, an Ulsterman, would have none of it. Important people need to be welcomed properly!

Two months later we had visitors from USAID, who explained that Bill and Hillary Clinton would be visiting Uganda in March. The American Government, through

USAID, had given 250,000 dollars to finance the Laboratory Assistant Training School at Kiwoko so our project was on their list of possible visits. Plans were set in motion for President Clinton to officially open the five buildings involved. 23 March was pencilled in the diary three days after I would officially become the new medical superintendent. A few days later the deputy ambassador came to discuss details. The ambassador herself made the final visit, accompanied by two White House interns. This was at the height of the Monica Lewinsky affair, and one of their priorities was to make the President look good on CNN. As the day approached the local policeman from Kiwoko village came to plan security, unaware that this was not his responsibility, but entirely under the control of the American Secret Service. After one of the many visits rumour spread that the shifty guy in the suit was a CIA agent rather than an Embassy official. Eventually the plug was pulled on the trip and the Clintons went elsewhere.

From one point of view it seemed a shame, but it might have been unduly stressful, as I had not had time to adjust to my new role including the niceties of speechifying on such occasions. The American ambassador returned as compensation for the non-appearance of the President. She had already had the tour of the hospital as a rehearsal for the President's anticipated visit, but now had a repeat of it in the company of various Ugandan dignitaries. Unaware of protocol for these events, I rapidly tied myself in knots. I welcomed the US Ambassador, thanked the US Government, gave my speech and sat down. At this point the hospital administrator enlightened me that I should have welcomed the local MP; at the conclusion of the next speech I duly did so. I then discovered that I had committed a further faux pas, having failed to welcome the local women's representative for the District; she was actually a minister and not just an MP. I spent the whole day trying to welcome everyone in order of importance. There was the LCV (local councillor, grade five) Chairman, the Head of Luwero District, but there was also an LCIV (for the County), an LCIII (for the Sub County), an LCII for the parish, and an LCI for Kiwoko village; in fact, if the President of Uganda himself visited, he could not have spoken without permission from the LCI. So I spent the day offending people of high and low estate, and trying to make up for it. Finally the US Ambassador gave a demonstration of how it should be done:

> 'Government and District leaders, religious leaders, hospital representatives, and all others, all protocol observed, greetings from . . .'

My wife Kate, along with some of the Americans, was killing herself with laughter at my performance. At lunch I sat next to the Ambassador, surrounded by important people. In order to properly welcome them I had to discover who they were; the list of names came piecemeal in dribs and drabs and I should have said, 'Enough is enough!' Those charged with making seating arrangements seemed to have had the same problem with protocol; the lunch was supposed to be attended by senior staff only, but one visitor later asked why he had been seated next to the man who cleaned the toilets!

The next VIP to visit was the First Lady, Mrs Janet Museveni. She came in July 1997 to open a community-based health care meeting hall sponsored by the ISIS Foundation. Preparing was an exciting time. Dogs searched our home for bombs and an enormous machine gun was installed in the garden, not to mention the day itself. She seemed to be impressed with what we were trying to do and after the visit wanted to suggest further projects. Out of her desire to help the people of the Luwero District, she later called together the heads of the United Nations Population Fund for Uganda and the Population Secretariat for Uganda, a Government body and set up a meeting. As we sat down she pointed to me and said to these important people, 'This is Dr Wooding, I want you to work with him.'

We began to plan ways to address the sexual health problems of the adolescents and pregnant women in the District. Uganda has the second highest fertility rate in the world, with an average of 6.9 children per woman. Maternal death during pregnancy and childbirth, however, is 200 times more likely in Uganda than for a woman in the UK. I have carried out several caesarean sections for the fourteenth delivery; by which time the muscle of the womb is thin and scarred, resulting in excessive bleeding and a very difficult operation. Untrained traditional birth attendants deliver two thirds of Ugandan children in the villages. Sometimes this is by necessity rather than choice, either because a trained person is too expensive or simply non-existent in a very rural area.

As I was escorting Mrs Museveni, she told me that reading *The Man With the Key Has Gone* was what had originally made her want to visit the hospital. She stopped right outside the female ward, which was part of the original Barbara Kelly Memorial Hospital and asked after Nakato, a woman who lived on the ward (read the story of Nakato in *The Man With the Key Has Gone*). Nakato had a wasting disease, wrongly assumed to be due to AIDS, and when she arrived was at death's door. She was nursed back to health, but meanwhile her home had been destroyed. Sometimes superstitious villagers do this when they believe that someone is a witch or has been bewitched. Nakato had been admitted while the female ward was under construction, and was still there years later, after it had been renovated and enlarged. She had contracted TB during her fifteen years at Kiwoko, survived it, and then developed diabetes. As she had virtually no muscle and was all skin and bones there was nowhere to inject insulin, so tablets were the only option – less effective, but they helped her to survive. As I was the medical superintendent she regarded me as her 'father'; Ian Clarke was her 'uncle'. I thought it would be a great honour for Nakato to meet the First Lady. The conversation went like this:

'Hello, how are you?'

'I am fine. How are you?'

'How wonderful. You speak English?'

That was the end of their conversation. Nakato only knew the greetings.

Kiwoko Hospital grew up in response to need and had not been planned as a 220-bedded hospital. The initial hospital building had no sluice, toilet, or side room. There was a children's ward, a female ward, an outpatient department, a pharmacy, and a theatre, all rolled into one. I saw it as my task to convert the hospital into a planned unit with proper facilities. In order to do this we rebuilt every ward, starting with the TB ward, followed by the paediatric ward, then a new male ward, then a special care baby unit and, finally, a reconstructed female ward. As we were leaving, yet another new TB ward was being built so that the cycle was beginning again.

Chapter 18

Close Encounters

> *Latet anguis in herba. (There's a snake hidden in the grass.)*
> (Virgil, 70–19 BC)

One day a puff adder was spotted in our garden. A swift blow to the head soon ended its life! I am not used to snakes and never know which ones are dangerous, but had no doubt this one definitely was! We seemed to be spotting more and more snakes. Another day our four-year-old daughter, Anna, was playing in the garden when we heard our son Ben, aged six, shouting at her to stay still. She had seen a snake slithering through the grass, and having seen people kill snakes, she went after it with a plastic ice-cream box, aiming to decapitate it. This was not the time to conduct a lengthy anatomical inspection to ascertain if it had teeth and no fangs (not poisonous) or fangs (poisonous). Eventually the danger was over when one of our staff ran up and killed it. Many Ugandans believe that you then have to burn a dead snake, or small snakes will appear from inside it. I don't believe this, my theory is that what they see are maggots feeding on the decomposing snake.

My worst snake experience happened at 9.30pm one night while I was operating. I heard Kate shout to me through the theatre window that there was a snake in the house; she was holding Anna, who was only seven weeks old, with Ben by her side. There was nothing I could do at that moment since I was in the middle of an operation. Kate went and found the administrator and a search of the whole house was carried out, but no snake was discovered. We spent the next two weeks not sure when or where we would meet the intruder. We were already under considerable stress without needing the fear of some terrible tragedy due to our uninvited guest. It was probably the lowest point for us. We were in the middle of protracted discussions with some of the members of the hospital board of governors with whom we disagreed about the structure of the hospital and its management. We also had just dismissed a student nurse who had a 'moral lapse'. Having been paying her school fees we felt personally involved. We felt we were under spiritual attack; perhaps the snake's presence made a fitting metaphor. Eventually we were able to call for prayer support. On the night people met to pray with us we were given assurance the spiritual attack was over and we did not need to continue to pray about the contentious matter. The next day the snake was found hiding in the larder and the issues to do with the hospital and the board were resolved at the board of governors meeting. Prayer is effective.

As we prepared to leave Kiwoko we had our final snake encounter. This time we did not actually see the snake. We had noticed, without paying much attention to, a hole at the bottom of our garden. One day, as I took the children for a walk, I spotted a seven-foot long snakeskin beside the hole. Unfortunately the seven foot long snake was not in residence. There was a lot of bushy growth nearby, so we dug out the hole and cleared the entire surrounding area but still with no snake. 'Well, at least we would be able to see it coming,' I thought.

Our close encounters with serpents were nothing compared to that of Livingstone, an eight-year-old boy, who was admitted to the hospital with a snake bite. He claimed that the snake had been inside his body. Since the opposite was more likely, we thought that he was suffering from a form of post-traumatic stress disorder. Livingstone persisted in the belief that the snake had entered his body where its teeth had punctured his skin. His mother explained that he had been walking through a forest when a python attacked him; it had coiled itself around him, except for his head, and was about to swallow him whole when some passers-by with machetes rescued him. The snake was alleged to have been sixty feet long and one metre across; the portion they took back to the village was twenty feet long. I was sceptical about these huge dimensions and also that that a python could swallow a boy.

Later when I mentioned this incident to American friend, he told me how he had seen a large python cut open, revealing a whole dead calf. Livingstone had ample reason for post-traumatic stress! Eventually he recovered enough to go home, but he is still too frightened to walk alone in the forest.

An old lady named Nalongo was working in her field one day when she was bitten on the hand by a snake. While not all snakebites are dangerous, some can paralyse the nerves so you cannot breathe; others stop the blood clotting so that you bleed to death. Others cause the soft tissues, skin, fat and muscle, to die (tissue necrosis) and this is what happened to Nalongo. She spent over a month in the hospital, during which time she had to have two dead fingers amputated. This cost £140 but, as a poor peasant farmer, she could not afford anything approaching that. She lived nearby so we visited her at home to make a financial assessment and wrote off the bill to the Good Samaritan Fund. Her son makes a modest income by making charcoal and, instead of the money, he gave us ten sacks of charcoal, worth about £20. We took Nalongo and her belongings home and brought back the sacks of charcoal. As we left she shouted out her thanks and praise to the hospital for the kindness that she had experienced.

A month after we left, in August 2003, a leopard attacked a farmer, grabbing his head in its mouth; the man said it felt like his head was going to explode. Some passers-by rescued him, and killed the leopard and took it to the Kiwoko police post. It became a tourist attraction for Kiwoko staff, although some of the British medical students initially chose not to join the throng. By the time they did, the leopard had been skinned and the bush-meat was being doled out. However, the local butcher offered to put the skin back on what was left so they could take good photographs!

Chapter 19

Made for Mission

> The salvation of the lost is not best accomplished by
> great popular campaigns, conducted by a small minority
> of specialists in public evangelism, but by the godly,
> honest witness of believers individually. It is pure
> irresponsibility to leave the evangelization of the lost to
> the 'experts,' as many are doing today. God would have
> every believer do his part to win the lost to Christ by
> prayer, personal witness and sincere godliness.
>
> (Cornelius Stam, 1909–2003)

Kiwoko is a light, a beacon of hope to the surrounding
area. Many of our staff are committed Christians and
have been going out to share their faith in the villages.
Many problems would be prevented if people would
live out the faith they profess. The only sure way to
avoid AIDS is moral living, by both partners in a
marriage relationship. AIDS could be eliminated within
a generation if people lived according to God's prescrip-
tion, but this requires repentance, a change of heart.
There is a saying in Uganda, 'in the daytime, people

believe what you say, but forget it at night, when temptations come'.

We formed a Kiwoko Mission Team to bring the gospel to people in the local area and I participated as far as commitments to family and patients permitted. We would go to a village and sometimes, on our first visit, the people would sit around drinking home brew beer. Many of these people attended church and called themselves Christians, but their lifestyles told a different story. Often, when we paid a return visit after some weeks they were prepared to listen.

I was patron but the team leader is Shadrach, a pharmacist at the hospital. He spoke to me one Monday following a weekend mission at a village called Bange.

'How was it?' I enquired.

'Fifty-six people made commitments, so we started meeting under a tree; someone let us use their home, so we have started a church.'

He gave me a quizzical look, suggesting that he was unsure if I would approve, since we were with CMS, an Anglican mission. I am an Anglican, but we also worshipped with the Ichthus Christian Fellowship in London, and thoroughly approved of church planting. I believe this is the best way to evangelise and see permanent change in people and in a community.

Denominationalism is a form of tribalism that has plagued Uganda for generations, and the different denominations often distrust each other, so we needed to be careful. Pentecostals sometimes advise people to leave the Church of Uganda when they have had a personal experience of salvation, rather than to stay on as salt and light. These issues are not unique to Africa. Churches in the West also need a fresh visitation of the Holy Spirit to bring renewal and revival.

When we had preached the gospel in a number of different villages I made a suggestion to Shadrach, 'I think you should go back to Bange and see how they are getting on.' We found that thirty of the original fifty-six remained committed. Some of these had previously earned their living by brewing alcohol and, having abandoned this occupation, were in financial difficulties. They needed practical help and advice as they established a new way of life; there was no pastor trained to guide them. We realised that we were registering decisions but failing to make disciples.

This led us into a new phase of ministry. A team from St Mary's, Bryanston Square, in London, had been coming each year to help with outreach. On their next visit we utilised them for follow up evangelism in Bange. I mentioned to their leaders that for a mere £300 they could buy the plot of land for the new Bange church building. Although St Mary's was itself undertaking expensive renovations they gave £3,000, so we were able to erect the building and install a new PA system as well. St Mary's contribution provided the cement and iron sheets (the larger expense); the community baked bricks, dug sand, sawed wood and built the church.

A year later we went returned with the St Mary's team for the formal opening of Bange Community Harvesters Church. As we listened to the speeches it was encouraging to hear the members of the community thank one another for their labours, rather than thanking us. This indicated that they had assumed responsibility and ownership, and would take care of ongoing repairs to the building; it had become theirs rather than ours. A further benefit was that the former brewers had developed an alternative, more constructive skill – making bricks. I issued a challenge to the infant church to plant more churches and reproduce the life they had received. At the end of 2003 we learned that this had begun to happen.

We held another mission in Matembe. An Anglican church there had originated in the Bazukufu (reawakened movement) of the East African Revival, but over the succeeding years it had become enmeshed in legalism. A Pentecostal Church had subsequently been formed, with about thirty members, but they needed some encouragement. I travelled there in a pickup truck with six visitors – five medical students and a nurse called William. During the journey he indicated a desire to make a recording of the hospital choir, and this happened a year later when St Mary's returned with an ethnomusicologist as part of their team. He looked after the technical side of the recording and William prepared the choirs, resulting in the Kiwoko CD, available on request.

Three of us were in the front of the vehicle and four on the back seat. In addition, in the rear of the vehicle was the body of a woman who had died of AIDS during the previous night, accompanied by her children. As we approached their village the children began to wail, alerting locals to the situation. The villagers were grateful for the care we had shown to their neighbour, but it was all very sad. She was the adult patient in the incident when I had to choose whether to give blood to her or to a child.

Two things impressed me at the Matembe mission. Daniel, one of the visiting medical students, knelt down on the platform and recounted how he had given his life to Christ when he was twelve years old, kneeling by the side of his bed. A villager looked at him and thought, 'If the *muzungu* (white man) is willing to kneel down in my village, this message must be important.' The other incident occurred after I had preached. A teacher came up to me, stating that he was a good Anglican, but smelling of alcohol. I told him he needed to repent and turn away from his drinking, and he gave himself to Christ. Soon after this I returned to Kiwoko with a full complement of passengers, while the others stayed on. I was not at all confident about the nature of the teacher's commitment, but I heard later that, at the evening meeting, he took out a bottle of spirits and poured it on the ground, stating he had found Christ and had finished with drink. Next day he was in the Pentecostal church 'in his right mind'. As a result of that weekend the church attendance doubled, people cramming inside the mud-walled, grass-thatched, building.

The hospital planted a total of five churches while I was medical superintendent. In addition, some of the surrounding churches asked to have a relationship with Kiwoko; this was because the Government wanted to crack down on churches springing up without a satisfactory structure of authority, in the wake of the Kanungu problems. Pentecostal churches were obliged to relate to one of several umbrella organisations. We did not want to start another denomination, especially as we are part of the Anglican Communion, so we encouraged these churches to join with another local organisation. Some link churches in the UK are raising funds to train local pastors. The first pastors conference was held in April 2005, where the main speaker was Roy Millar, the Chairman of Friends of Kiwoko. One hundred and seventy pastors, both Anglican and Pentecostal, went. In this way we can safeguard new churches from going astray. Our role is to act as facilitator rather than being a funding organisation.

Two other medical students, Andrew and Alistair, were really passionate about mission, and shared their faith on the wards every Wednesday night. On one occasion they spoke to a man who was dying of AIDS and he gave his life to Christ. The nurses noticed a marked improvement in his behaviour, before his death four days later. On another occasion, at a village, they met a woman who had never seen a white person. She thought, 'If these white people were willing to come to my village they must have a very important message,' and gave her life to Christ.

Forty-eight people responded one night when we showed a film about the life of Jesus. It was amazing to observe the crowd watching the *Jesus* film, and hearing Jesus speak in their own language. They cheered when an evil spirit was cast out, and expressed their sadness as Jesus was crucified. They shouted for joy when he rose from the tomb, bringing new life to those who receive him! I realised how much we take this message for granted. It is clear to me, as I work once again in the UK where there is so much divorce and so many stress-related diseases, that a relationship with Jesus is the solution to the prevailing ills of our society.

Chapter 20

Stress and Satisfaction

> *When I stand before God at the end of my life, I would hope that I would not have a single bit of talent left, and could say, 'I used everything you gave me.'*
>
> (Erma Louise Bombeck, b. 1927)

Kate and I really enjoyed our time at Kiwoko. We saw great developments; some twenty-five buildings were constructed or hugely renovated including a new operating theatre, male ward, nurse accommodation, a rebuilt female ward, a pharmacy and a paediatric ward. Staff were trained; some went on courses to upgrade their qualifications and returned with new skills. When we first arrived in Kiwoko a TB (tuberculosis) ward was under construction. As we left six years later a TB ward was under construction. There was an important difference; the new TB ward is actually the third one. As the hospital has expanded, it has repeatedly approached the existing TB ward. TB is infectious and should, therefore, be on the outskirts of the hospital.

After we arrived we used to hear some of the

Ugandans say that God has a special place in his heart for Kiwoko. This was hard to understand until we had been there for a time and observed for ourselves that it is true. Visitors commented that they sensed the presence of God. Some of this is probably related to intercession by staff and others for the hospital. Barney Coombs, a close friend of Barbara Kelly in whose memory the original finance had been contributed, prayed at the site of the initial foundations at Kiwoko that God would do a great work. He called the hospital 'an Isaac' (a child of promise).

Living and working at Kiwoko caused our faith to grow as we saw God at work. By the end of my first year the expenditure was £15,000 more than the total income. I knelt by my bed and prayed for that £15,000; next day a letter arrived promising the whole amount. On another occasion I prayed for £10,000. This time it did not arrive so promptly but I kept on praying, and a little later someone gave the whole amount; God answered at the right time. When I checked my journal I found that it arrived the day after I had promised to raise the wages of all of the staff, not knowing where the money would come from. Money came in as needed, staff were always paid on time and we never turned patients away, even though 70% of the running costs depended on donations. It proved to us the truth that God is able to do much, much more than we ask or think. In his book Ian Clarke called it the widow's barrel. God was equally faithful to us.

Money was not the only area where we saw God was at work. One of the more stressful incidents was when

Sue Hocking, our nurse tutor and one of the founding members of Kiwoko Hospital, developed ovarian cancer and had to return to the UK at short notice. The nursing school could not continue to function in the absence of a nurse tutor. We managed to find a part-time tutor and on her first day in post, we had a surprise inspection from the Ministry of Education. I was so glad I could introduce her as our tutor. Some time later we were informed during another surprise inspection that we could not run the school with only a part-time tutor. It coincided with the first day that a new full-time tutor was in post! As she took the inspectors on a tour of the hospital, I thought to myself, 'Lord, You love me and look after me so much; just when I could really have got it in the neck, You saved the day!'

On 26 January 2002 we had the graduation ceremony for the first enrolled nurses ever to be trained by Kiwoko Hospital. The British High Commissioner and the Director General of the Ministry of Health were present. Ian Clarke had trained local people to be nurse-aides from the inception of the hospital because no outsiders would come and work in a war-torn area. This developed into a two-year training programme, training nurses of such high quality that it was eventually upgraded to a nationally accredited enrolled nursing course. Some of the original nurse-aides enrolled on this programme, and all twenty-one students who took the exams passed with credit. This has been a remarkable achievement and the school must rank as one of the best in the country. Sue Hocking had to return to the UK for treatment but not before the graduation ceremony of her first cohort of trainees. How thankful we all were that she was there to experience the first fruits of her labour. Sadly Sue died in 2005.

God has always provided on time but usually with little time to spare. For instance, on the medical side, Richard was there to succeed Ian when he had to return home with ill health, Donald succeeded Richard, and I succeeded Donald. In a similar way David and Linda Hodgson came to replace Alan and Jean Casebow in the finance department. More recently the responsibilities of the medical superintendent were divided between two disciplines as the task had outgrown the capacity of a single person. A Ugandan doctor, James Nnyonyintono, became medical superintendent, a sign that the hospital had come of age. Jim McAnlis in the new and parallel post of programmes manager took over the business and organisational side of the work. His wife, Margaret, took over Kate's role looking after visitors and medical students staying at the guesthouse.

We have seen churches planted and people find faith. We have seen lives saved and know that we have made a difference. It is a feeling that is very hard to describe, but it is akin to the sense of satisfaction after a good meal. We can both say that our time in Kiwoko was very rewarding. We had the privilege of leading a wonderful team of dedicated men and women and saw God at work touching every aspect of people's lives. Our experiences there have left an indelible mark upon us. On one occasion someone prophesied over Kate and me that we had been branded with Kiwoko.

We are still pondering what that means in practical terms. Meanwhile we will support the hospital through the Friends of Kiwoko.

Once, after I spoke about our deep sense of attachment to Kiwoko, someone responded with the question, 'Why did you leave?' I had to have an answer that would satisfy not only him, but also me. Kate and I had always felt that we should spend two three-year terms on the mission field. We did not know precisely why, but that is what we felt. It was this conviction that kept us in Kiwoko when we were severely tested during our third year there and were in conflict with the hospital board. Because of our differences of opinion one of the board members wrote to CMS suggesting that we should return following our leave period only as a last resort, that is, if they were unable to find anyone else to fill the gap. When I heard this I thought, 'What's the point of giving some of the best years of my life to a project where I am not appreciated?' When difficulties like that arise it is easy to get things out of proportion. When I had had time to reflect I realised that most people were warm and friendly towards us and appreciated our contribution to the life of the hospital. I had given too much weight to negative comments from one quarter. CMS did send us back with their blessing.

On our second tour things were much better, but 2002 was definitely our *annus horribilis*. Late in the evening on 7 January I pricked myself with a needle while performing a caesarean section. In these circumstances I always followed the practice of testing the mother for HIV and on all previous occasions the test had been negative; this time the patient was HIV positive. The needle had not penetrated deeply, but I still took the precaution of taking anti-retroviral drugs for a month to reduce the risk of becoming HIV positive. I needed to commence this treatment within the hour, so at midnight I woke Kate, told her what had happened, and we prayed. I swallowed the tablets and went back to the wards to see an admission. The recommendation is that, when possible, you should take the first tablet in the evening. I soon discovered why: I started to feel very dizzy and became muddled in my thinking while examining the patient. Following this I prayed for a quiet night; my prayers were answered but I slept poorly. The drugs cause insomnia, so I spent a whole month feeling washed out and achieving very little. Anti-retroviral therapy reduces the risk of becoming HIV positive from 0.4% down to 0.1%. It is only after three months and a repeat HIV test, that the outcome becomes known. This risk appears small until it becomes personal. My anxiety was heightened by the implications for Kate and our children, but deep down I discovered the thought at the back of my mind that if I did become HIV positive I knew it would not be the end of God's purposes for me. The definitive test at the end of three months was negative, for which I shall always be grateful.

That same month, January 2002, there was a robbery at the hospital farm, the second one that year. When the police investigated it appeared to be an inside job. One of the managers was arrested and was subsequently dismissed. He had been our friend so that discovery was painful for us. The day after his dismissal the ambulance developed a mechanical fault and crashed, resulting in a bill of nearly £1,000 for repairs.

On the same day Sue Hocking, principal tutor in the nurse training school, was diagnosed with ovarian cancer one of her students had had to have her right thumb amputated because of malignant melanoma. That same week a child in Kampala had run onto a road and one of our vehicles had knocked him down, resulting in a fracture of his foot. During the following weeks I and three other members of our expatriate staff found that there had been fraudulent attempts to transfer money from our bank accounts; the UK banks became suspicious and intervened to prevent any financial loss.

Following this troubled period things seemed to be settling down. Then on Wednesday 5 June staff went to Kampala as usual to purchase essential drugs. They had just changed £2,500 into Ugandan shillings when a vehicle pulled up in front of their car and three armed robbers jumped out, pointing guns at the heads of Sula the driver and Robinah, who was to make the purchases. During the previous month there had been ten robberies in Kampala, usually targeting business people and many of them had been fatally wounded. The practise of thieves in Uganda is to shoot first and then rob, in case there is an armed guard in the car, so Robinah and Sula were in real danger. Robinah tried to hide the money, but it was spotted and she wisely handed it all over. It is better to lose money than life. Unfortunately the police were not interested in investigating; instead they threatened to arrest our staff. They may have thought that there had been collusion between the robbers and the robbed or perhaps they were hoping for a bribe.

When some of my relatives heard about all these difficulties they thought, and told us, it was time we came home. I had been reading about Brother Yun, called the Heavenly Man, and like him had arrived at a conviction: when things get tough God is more real. He had discovered this in China, and so had I on a much smaller scale. Why are we so stubborn that it sometimes takes the megaphone of pain and hardship before we learn that God is in charge and uses His people to accomplish His purposes? Do you realise that this is often the situation with people under pressure in isolated situations? After the needle-stick injury I found it difficult to pray for myself, but many people assured me of their prayers. God's care for us was expressed in the actions of His people as churches rallied around and took up collections to replace the money that had been stolen and to repair the ambulance. I have discovered in practice that God provides the right people at the right time and the right answers at the right time. All the difficulties have been valuable; we have seen our God at work, turning difficulties into opportunities. We have experienced God's unfailing love, and been better able to share the Good News. It is impossible to share effectively what you have not personally experienced.

When our second term was nearing conclusion we had to make a decision. We had a growing conviction that we should return to Oxford, as we subsequently did.

We knew that we would step outside God's will if we stayed on in Kiwoko merely on the grounds that we had succeeded in overseeing the rapid growth and development of the work. We were aware of the possibility of burnout; living in a foreign culture causes stress. In the early days there were neither phone lines nor e-mail, without which there is a feeling of isolation from friends and family and this takes its toll. I was 'the boss' on site, with ultimate responsibility for everything; I could only share with friends among the staff to a limited extent as some of the problems involved other staff members. By the time our first leave came round our stress levels had become uncomfortable and needed attention. Other missionaries shared with us that even in situations where there is a sizable group of expatriate fellow Christian workers, a major cause of stress remains – the dynamics of the group itself. It can be like living in a hothouse with limited opportunities to escape. Clearly there is no safety in numbers. The educational and social needs of our two children Ben and Anna were additional concerns. Up to that time home schooling had been very satisfactory, with input from Vicky Anderson from Northern Ireland and Lindsay Beitz from Canada who volunteered to assist. Now the time was approaching when social interaction with other children would be important. The available solutions were boarding school, which we did not consider appropriate, or a move to Kampala, which would effectively sever our relationship with rural Kiwoko.

Conviction about our calling and concern for Ben and Anna seemed to be converging. Consequently we telephoned a headmistress in England and asked if she would reserve a place Ben for the following year, and she immediately agreed; we took this as a sort of confirmation.

There was to be one final stress – the succession. I once heard someone say, 'Success is succession.' During the second three-year term I had prayed for a successor and written to potential people about it. Missionary doctors are harder to find now because medical students can end up owing more than £20,000 on qualifying and there is a much more clearly defined career ladder than was previously the case. We wondered about the feasibility of an expatriate project manager sharing leadership with a Ugandan medical superintendent. The task had become too big for one person to handle and different skills were now needed for effective management of the hospital. We had trained local doctors who were fully equipped to assume respon- sibility for medical leadership and who also shared the spiritual life and vision that are integral to the whole project. In this sense the hospital had come of age. Ian Clarke suggested just the person to take on the admin- istrative role – his brother-in-law, Jim McAnlis. I filed this away in my mind for future consideration.

In the summer of 2002 I attended a missionary conference in England under the auspices of the Ichthus Christian Fellowship, London. There was a prophecy and prayer time one evening for overseas missionaries and we were given two words:

The first message was that God would answer my prayers before our return to Kiwoko. That was only two weeks away, so I wondered if He would reveal the identity of my successor. The following week we travelled to Ireland to the Friends of Kiwoko Hospital AGM. During the few days we spent there we met Jim and Margaret McAnlis; they seemed ideal for the task at Kiwoko, but were not available because of work and other commitments. Soon after this Jim was released from his longstanding job. On the same day CMSI (the Church Missionary Society, Ireland) called him to discuss the post at Kiwoko Hospital. God's timing is perfect.

The second word we received was also appropriate, 'I should worry less about succession and more about values.' This made sense; if the hospital was run according to biblical values and if this worldview was fully owned by the staff, God would provide the right person to lead the work. Whoever succeeded me would, in any case, be changed by the experience of being in the hospital environment. I had been reflecting a lot on values after reading about Hudson Taylor, missionary to China; he led the China Inland Mission by faith and without making appeals for money. He said, 'God's work done in God's way will never lack God's resources.' My task was to discover what God wanted to achieve and find out how to do it in His way.

Epilogue

Making a Difference

> *He who chooses the beginning of the road chooses the place it leads to. It is the means that determines the end.*
>
> (Harry Emerson Fosdick, 1878–1969)
>
> *The world breaks everyone and afterwards many are strongest at the broken places.*
>
> (Ernest Hemingway, 1898–1961)
>
> *For all sad words of tongue or pen,*
> *The saddest are these: 'It might have been'.*
>
> (John Greenleaf Whittier, 1807–92)

There are seven principles I share from Bible verses that are very important to me. Every morning we would start our day with morning prayers. Before I left I spent some time sharing God's values from these verses with the staff.

First, we need to be born again, or saved, as it would be termed in Uganda:

'In reply Jesus declared, "I tell you the truth, no-one can see the kingdom of God unless he is born again."'

(John 3:3)

Secondly, the importance of world evangelism:

'Then Jesus came to them and said, "All authority in heaven and on earth has been given to me. Therefore go and make disciples of all nations, baptising them in the name of the Father and of the Son and of the Holy Spirit, and teaching them to obey everything I have commanded you. And surely I am with you always, to the very end of the age."'

(Matthew 28:18–20)

Thirdly, the importance of reaching out to the poor and needy.

Christianity has often been presented as a ticket to heaven, rather than a way of life, as salt and light that transforms society. However, when referring to King Josiah, the Bible has this to say:

'"Does it make you a king
*   to have more and more cedar?*
Did not your father have food and drink?
*   He did what was right and just,*
*   so all went well with him.*
He defended the cause of the poor and needy,
*   and so all went well.*
Is that not what it means to know me?"
*   declares the LORD.*

> *"But your eyes and your heart*
> *are set only on dishonest gain,*
> *on shedding innocent blood*
> *and on oppression and extortion." '*
>
> (Jeremiah 22:15–17)

When I first read this I realised that I cannot claim to know God yet ignore the needs of the poor. Much of what we tried to do in Kiwoko, with orphan sponsorship and the Good Samaritan Fund, was an outworking of that conviction.

Fourthly, apart from a right attitude to God, to those who don't know Christ, and to the poor, we need to have a right attitude to money:

> 'Two things I ask of you, O LORD;
>   do not refuse me before I die:
> Keep falsehood and lies far from me;
>   give me neither poverty nor riches,
>   but give me only my daily bread.
> Otherwise, I may have too much and disown you
>   and say, "Who is the LORD?"
> Or I may become poor and steal,
>   and so dishonour the name of my God.'
>
> (Proverbs 30:7–9)

Fifthly, there is the need for personal holiness and integrity, especially when dealing with other people's money:

> 'for it is written: "Be holy, because I am holy." '
>
> (1 Peter 1:16)

> *'And do not swear by your head, for you cannot make even one hair white or black. Simply let your "Yes" be "Yes", and your "No", "No"; anything beyond this comes from the evil one.'*
>
> (Matthew 5:36–37)

Sixthly, the need to be a good father and husband in your own family which God has given you.

> *'Fathers, do not exasperate your children; instead, bring them up in the training and instruction of the Lord.'*
>
> (Ephesians 6:4)

Lastly, we are called to service.

> *'Now that I, your Lord and Teacher, have washed your feet, you also should wash one another's feet.'*
>
> (John 13:14)

> *'Whatever you do, work at it with all your heart, as working for the Lord, not for men, since you know that you will receive an inheritance from the Lord as a reward. It is the Lord Christ you are serving.'*
>
> (Colossians 3:23–24)

It is difficult to maintain all of these within our own culture, especially with regard to money, possessions and power. My mother came to visit us a couple of months before we left, and advised us not to watch television when we returned home because so many of the programmes were about home improvement, gardening or cookery. She was right; these pander to a self-indulgent materialistic consumer culture, which, like acid rain, erodes our value system. This is why, on our first Christmas back at home, we bought most people second-hand presents and gave what we would have spent to Friends of Kiwoko Hospital. This has to be balanced by the fact that our God is a God of plenty, who wants to bless abundantly, who supplies all our needs; He is not the God of mediocrity, but He wants us to have no other gods before Him; so we will all keep on having to engage in an on-going battle with consumerism and the love of money.

The words of Ian Clarke on 19 March 1998, when I became medical superintendent, have remained with me. He felt that he had done something good with his life by establishing Kiwoko hospital and had been able to make a difference. He has had a serious cancer and has had to have chemotherapy twice, once after the original diagnosis and again for a recurrence of the tumour. He realises that life may be very short so we should make it count. Kate and I also feel that we have done something good with our lives by working at Kiwoko and that we, too, have made a difference. I would like to dedicate my final words to Ian Clarke for what he has achieved, but even more I thank God for giving us the opportunity to be used in His service.

Chapter 20½

What Katy Did

> I don't want to get to the end of my life and find
> that I have just lived the length of it. I want to have
> lived the width of it as well.
>
> (Diane Ackerman, b. 1948)

As you know, my wife is called Kate. I dedicate this book to her. She is outgoing, bold, diminutive, strong, quiet – but only at times, humorous, loving, scolds me when necessary, supports me all the time and I can find no line that best describes her than this:

> The LORD God said, "It is not good for the man to be alone. I will make a helper suitable for him." '
>
> (Genesis 2:18)

He did, and so this book gives her the last word.

Nick and I set off for Kiwoko in 1997 when Ben, our first child, was four months old. Since the time of our first leave in the UK people have repeatedly asked,

'What was it like to bring up a child in Uganda? Were you not worried about his health, diseases like malaria being so common there?' I would reply that we needed to put our trust in God. He was watching over us and we were in His hands. Some Westerners behave in a blasé fashion as if they are immune to everything. We were not naïve about potentially serious diseases and took proper precautions, but were not unduly anxious about Ben and he came to no harm. A baby with fever in Uganda should be suspected of having malaria, and a simple blood test proves or disproves this. Ben did, in fact, contract malaria but with prompt treatment he was back to normal within twelve hours.

Most Africans love children. It was a very enriching experience to raise our two children in that culture, Anna being born two years into our first term. Ben and I used to go to the hospital gate where the local *dukkas* (shops) were located to buy our staple provisions. Rice came in a large sack and needed to be sorted for stones when we arrived home. Flour came in two varieties, one for baking cakes and maize flour for making *posho*, a kind of porridge. It was a far cry from the pre-packaged world of Tesco and Marks & Spencer!

As the medical superintendent's wife I was able to create my own role, applying the skills I had acquired. This involved administration, hospitality, and supervising short-term visitors. Some expatriate visitors arrived when we had hardly had time to settle in ourselves; three were medical and one an administrator. It rapidly became clear to me that someone needed to co-ordinate and oversee the expatriate visitors' programme, and that someone seemed to be me! I was based at home caring for a young child, and so was in a position to make visitors welcome and find out how they were getting on. Many people enquired about visiting the hospital and, having accepted them, we needed to provide a structure for their visits so that they could have the best personal experience guide and also have exposure to areas where they could have practical input, then or later. We ourselves had initially come on a short visit and were inspired to return. Different people would respond in different ways; some would sense a call to mission work in Africa, others would pray and give practical support; hopefully everyone would be challenged and blessed with some fresh vision for their lives. In fact we saw these things happen over the subsequent six years.

The role of welcoming visitors gradually became a major task. During 1997 there were about twenty visitors who each stayed a few weeks, in 2002 there were more than a hundred, excluding day visitors. The greatest number was of expatriate medical students on electives ranging from six to eight weeks in length. The busiest times for me were when teams came to assist with various programmes. We would host the first meal in our home. I would then give them an induction, information about their stay, and take them on a tour of the hospital lasting several hours. The guest-house was located only thirty yards from our house so that I was near at hand to answer questions and supervise each programme. Each medical student was introduced to a doctor on the wards for further orientation and supervision.

It was vital for medical students to start on the correct footing and make sure that they were adequately supported as they encountered challenging experiences, often for the first time. Medical students from the West may not previously have been close to death, let alone the death of a child and sometimes they would see a young child die on their first day on the wards. They were also involved in situations where they had helped to treat or even resuscitate patients who subsequently died. It was important to have somewhere to go and someone available to talk to as they were adjusting to their emotional reactions and seeking to come to terms with situations. Our home was open for them to come and have a coffee and talk about these issues. They would have thoughts like 'If I had been more experienced I could have done more and that patient would not have died.' They needed to know that they were not yet qualified doctors and that their assistance to the medical staff was valuable and really appreciated, and that in any situation we can only do our best. Kiwoko hospital is a strong Christian community where we encountered ultimate questions of life and death on a daily basis and where these young people could mature as they wrestled with these issues in a supporting environment. It was a tremendous privilege to see many medical students grow in confidence and maturity over the course of a couple of months; some came to faith or were strengthened in it, and left with a clearer sense of purpose.

Donors were another important group of visitors. Sometimes it was an official visit from a donor organisation such as Compassion Canada (about twenty of them visited about twice a year), or the Farmers Overseas Action Group. On arrival they would gather on our veranda for sodas (soft drinks) and some home cooked biscuits. This would be followed by a tour of the hospital lasting about two hours, and further refreshments before leaving for Kampala, about one and a quarter hours journey away. The tour was the ideal setting to recall how the hospital had begun. We began at the Church of Uganda church building 500 yards away, and explained how patients had queued all around the building in those early days as they waited to see Ian Clarke. During the tour I would explain the huge difference in healthcare between Uganda and Western countries. There are no GP clinics here; people often delay seeking medical help, then travel for hours and arrive at hospital in a critical state with reduced prospect for survival.

I always made a special point of introducing visitors to members of staff, to shake hands, to greet, to encounter a smile and, even briefly, to feel a part of this special community. Ugandans are warm and friendly and make you feel special and appreciated, as much in greetings as in words. We wanted visitors to appreciate the quality of our staff for they are the real resource of the hospital.

Visitors were always introduced to Jajja and Nakato. Jajja is the name for grandmother in Luganda. They reminded me of the story of the Billy Goats Gruff who, as they walked across the bridge, had to pass the troll. Jajja was always sitting outside her mud hut as we walked towards the nurse training school; there was no possibility of passing her before she greeted everyone. She was now more than seventy years of age but supported her many grandchildren in their education, all her children having died of AIDS. Her little house, behind which she cooked trotters, was falling apart, but she was always cheerful and had a wonderful laugh. She typified many of the Ugandans we knew; very hard working and poor, yet full of infectious joy. Nick has already written about Nakato.

A vital part of my role was supporting Nick in his incredibly demanding job. We lived on site, and the operating theatre was only one hundred yards from our home. As well as his medical work, involving daily ward rounds, plus nights and weekends on call, Nick was responsible for giving leadership to and supervising all the hospital staff, teaching the more junior medical staff, interacting with donors, writing proposals and follow-up reports, and attending Ministry of Health meetings in his official capacity as medical superintendent. During our time the hospital grew from a small family unit of staff to a larger operational unit requiring job descriptions, policies and more defined management structures.

Kiwoko hospital is a special place, a community where people live and work together and it was a great privilege to feel part of it. There were no walls with barbed wire between houses or security guards to segregate us, as is the case in Kampala. A friend had given us excellent advice, 'Make space for nationals.' It is easier to communicate with another person from your own culture, but making friends with Ugandans was very special for us and was something we will always treasure. These friendships developed by playing a guitar together, or asking advice, and in the process we learned about their culture and were made to feel at home. A number of women worked at different times in our home and special friendships developed as we shared our lives together, in spite of very different backgrounds of race and culture.

Nick and I learned to trust God in a great many situations and we experienced His faithfulness. For example, in Uganda, where the roads are so dangerous and the car may look rather dodgy, it is natural to commit the journey to God; by contrast it is unusual to pray before setting out on a car journey in the UK although the possibility of an accident exists. In many ways it was easier to trust God in Kiwoko, having seen Him answer prayers in situations where people had nowhere else to turn. In the West we are cushioned in so many ways and this can create the illusion of security; we are surrounded by creature comforts, insurance etc. and so we tend to put our trust in these rather than remembering that God ultimately provides for our needs. Ugandan Christians offer a challenging example; despite having very little they trust in God's promises and provision. We can be part of the supply chain as God responds to their prayers.

> *Life is a library owned by an author. It has a few books which he wrote himself, but most of them were written for him.*
>
> (Harry Emerson Fosdick, 1878–1969)

Copies of this book and Ian Clarke's book, *The Man With the Key Has Gone*, are available from:

'Friends of Kiwoko Hospital'
30 The Close
Marino
Holywood
N. Ireland BT18 0AW

Web site: http://www.fokh.org.uk

We hope you enjoyed reading this New Wine book.
For details of other New Wine books
and a range of 2,000 titles from other
Word and Spirit publishers visit our website:
www.newwineministries.co.uk